Praise for The Official Gui
Primary Care Practice:

"Dr. Farrago should be against the laws of thermodynamics. He is a perpetual motion machine. Always innovating and finding new ways to advocate for patients. His book will help any physician transition into direct primary care."

Vance Lassey, MD Holton Direct Care

"I wish I'd had this book when starting my direct care practice! It is a very valuable resource, packed with practical advice on nearly every aspect of starting a Direct Primary Care practice. Dr Farrago's wit, wisdom, and enthusiasm shine through on every page."

Dr Michael Garrett, M.D. Owner, Direct MD Austin

This book will give you all the information you need to start your own DPC practice. I started mine last year and couldn't have done it without this book. Dr. Farrago's writing style is conversational and witty, and you won't be able to put it down, which is an incredibly weird thing to say about a book on practice management.

Emily O'Rourke, MD

Dr. Farrago has a knack for identifying and describing the ills that plague primary care medicine. He is a champion as well as a model for the solution: Direct Primary Care. His book thoroughly and succinctly outlines the purpose, the process, and the problems of starting a DPC practice .

Saleh R Shahid, MD

Looking for some top notch advice from someone who is actually practicing Direct Primary care? You need to read this book. Dr. Farrago started the popular blog Authentic Medicine 14 years ago where he is constantly pointing out how ridiculous our current healthcare system is and standing up for doctors. If you need some courage to be able to give your hospital administrators the middle finger and start practicing medicine the way YOU want to, buy this book now

Luke Van Kirk, DO

iii

CONTENTS

v

PREAMBLE

It's been over five years since the first edition of this book was published. Direct Primary Care was in its infancy. Heck, when I started my practice, there were less than a hundred practices. When I retired there were thousands. I am proud to think this book was a small part of that, and that it helped a lot of people. I retired from clinical practice in 2020 (yes, the year of the pandemic but that was not the cause) and sold my practice to a great doctor. I put that information in this book. But I also felt that I needed to update a lot of things. Resources have surged and changed. Personally, I wrote two other books (*The Direct Primary Care Doctor's Daily Motivational Journal* and *Slowing the Churn in Direct Primary Care While Also Keeping Your Sanity*), which I highly recommend you get. Others physicians have also written books, and I know all these authors personally. Should you buy my other books? Yes! Should you buy the books written by other DPC docs? Yes! Why? Because you need all the information you can get even if some information is repeated. Think of it as reinforcement for a very big venture where you need all the confidence you can get.

I tried to add as much information that I could to this updated version, but I am sure I am missing some. DPC is still young and is changing by the day. There were not many podcasts when I started. Now there are many. There were not many EMRs made just for DPC. Now there are many. I have chosen NOT to list everything due to the fluctuation and instability in the market. You will do just fine without having this information as you will always be able to search for it on your own. I think the best way to view this book is as a kick in the pants. Most of the feedback I have gotten over the years is how this book motivated people to start their own DPC practice, and how thankful they were to have this book. I am honored and flattered by this. After two years in practice, you will NOT need this book anymore as you will be an expert. This does not mean you are in the clear, and there always hiccups or valleys in your journey. That is why I wrote those other two books. They will make more sense when you get there.

The future is bright for you and for Direct Primary Care. It is getting better each day. I hope I can help you in this adventure and that you can be the doctor you always wanted to be.

SECTION ONE

So You Are Toying with The Idea of
Starting Your Own DPC
Practice?

1. Introduction

"I just want to help people." That was the line used by so many of us when we interviewed for medical school. I am sure it is still used by prospective students today. I mean you couldn't say that you wanted to make money. You couldn't say that you wanted the prestige of becoming a doctor. Nope. It was all about helping people. This is NOT to say that there isn't a kernel of truth in the helping part. For most, it truly is the real reason they wanted to be physicians. And once they got into medical school, reality bit them right in the ass. Since you are a doctor who is reading this, then I do not have to rehash how much work we did. It turns out that succeeding and surviving somehow made us table that "helping" ideology dream. When it came to choosing a residency dare I say that maybe, just maybe those who chose family medicine or pure internal medicine may have found that altruistic urge again? This can be debated but it is doesn't really matter. After residency, we were thrust into the world of hospital employers and third-party payers. We were their minions and this took away from helping or serving others. We were treating numbers and being told how to practice. Well, I am here to tell you that this book is for those doctors who still want to help people. This book is for those doctors who feel it is okay to earn money. This book is for those doctors who want to feel proud that they are doctors. This book is for those doctors who want to control their own lives and not be pawns that the hospital CEO places where he or she wants. This book is about freedom because you can have all of that. The only way to accomplish this, however, is to start your own direct primary care practice.

So who am I to write a direct primary care book? Well, I'm a physician who did direct primary care. Plain and simple. I wasn't the first. I won't be the last. I may have been the most vocal, though. I had been blogging about the crap going on in our healthcare system for 14 years and had always sung the praises of DPC. I even published a humorous medical magazine, the Placebo Journal, for ten years. I was just too much of a wimp to make the plunge. That changed in 2014. I burned the boats, kicked away the ladders (insert any other metaphor here), and started my practice from scratch in Forest, Virginia. I didn't have the advantage of converting an established practice to DPC so I had a big hill to climb. I was also an old man, in my fifth decade, when I decided to make this change. That means at a time when most docs are looking toward retirement or just living with the bullshit of today's healthcare system, I was starting a new chapter in my life. I was also new in the community where I started this. All of these things made the odds of success lower and lower. But I said "f$ck it" and took the risk and…..I succeeded! And you can too.

Why Did I Succeed?

To be honest, I did have some things in my favor. I am in an area that's definitely upper-middle-class in some sections so I knew that if DPC didn't work here, then it really wouldn't work anywhere. This wasn't luck because I moved from Maine to this place in Virginia to give myself that advantage. You know what they say - luck is where preparation meets opportunity. I was prepared for when the opportunity came. You should be as well.

I also am somewhat of a risk taker by nature and can be tenacious in getting the things I want. I therefore convinced myself that if I couldn't do it, then nobody could. I also hated the present healthcare model so much that I knew there was no going back. I decided that I would outwork anybody if that is what it took to succeed. Despite some local gamesmanship and political maneuvering by a local FP group, I was still able to work around it and grow my practice. Why? I had no choice. If I was going to be the physician I always wanted to be, then I was going to either give it my all and succeed in direct primary care or quit this job altogether. I opted out of Medicare and Medicaid, which meant there was no moonlighting or working for anyone else for at least two years. Like I said, I burned the boats behind me, which meant supreme leverage and pressure on me to make this dream a reality.

Why I Was Confident This Concept Would Work?

The concept of DPC was not new to me. I always believed insurance companies were ripping people off even back when I was in residency in the mid 90s. And that is nothing compared to what they are doing now! Back then I felt I could be my own mini HMO to cover just the primary portion of a patients care, which is 90% of all their healthcare. That concept was basically direct primary care. Even then I was collecting all the articles I could on what was called "cash pay practices." It's funny. I still have the folder today and many of those concepts hold true. Unfortunately, I had too much school debt back then and succumbed to the temptation of being employed by a hospital in Maine. Luckily, I had great partners and the job of being a family doctor was initially fun. It was different back then. There were no quality metrics and less administrators were involved. There were no EMRs, no justification for orders, and no prior authorizations. Also, I was young and ready to churn through patients each day because I was brainwashed into thinking that was what family doctors do. Unfortunately, the job kept changing. Suffice it to say, that after being a pawn in the chess set of two different employers for 15 years, I decided enough was enough. There was so much in Maine I liked. My patients were good, and many remain my friends to this day. I did love working with my partners as we were best friends and spent a ton of time commiserating. The problem was that healthcare was getting worse and the issues were unsolvable as an employed doc. The time with my partners became bitch sessions that led to nowhere. I needed to move on.

In 2012, I decided to move closer to my wife's family in Virginia. I was getting too old for the frigid weather in Maine. I also, as noted above, wanted to find the right community that could support a DPC practice. I initially took a job at an urgent care center so they could pay for my moving expenses and a bonus. I needed that influx of cash. Unfortunately, that job wasn't for me either. After a year of seeing up to 70 patients per day, which sucked my life away, I needed out. I was tempted into being an employed family doctor again as there are always jobs available for our specialty. I thought I would give it one more shot at seeing if primary care with a local private group would work. It didn't. I hired myself out as an independent contractor, and the people and staff were great but the healthcare model was the same...broken. I call it industrialized medicine because it is similar to the industrialized food model. Doctors have to grind through patients as well as try to fill mandates that have nothing do with patient care. This was not the picture that I had of being a doctor when I was a medical student and it is still not today. It turns out that the picture I had in my mind was being a direct primary care doctor.

So I took the leap into DPC. The good news was that no one was doing direct primary care in my community. The bad news that no one was doing direct primary care my community. That meant I had to really make a name for myself and get out and market myself because the concept was unknown. Isn't that ridiculous, a concept where a patient directly pays the doctor or a customer directly pays the owner is unheard of? This is where we have gotten in our healthcare system. It's warped.

As I said, my personality lends itself to taking these leaps because I don't mind taking risks. It's just in my nature. For other people, it's hard, which makes starting a DPC difficult. I am not here to shake you and make you do something you don't want to do. Direct primary care will not be the job for you; however, if you can't take risks. It is for the person who is willing to go out on a limb, be innovative, and disrupt healthcare. If this is you, then I welcome you into our club and I will do anything to help you succeed. Why? Because you are NOT competition and you will help spread the word about DPC. It is my feeling that a rising tide floats all boats, and so if you succeed then we all succeed.

So are you ready to take a risk? Are you ready to go out on a limb? Are you ready to innovate and disrupt healthcare? Are you ready to truly help people like you wanted to do when you were in medical school? Are you ready to start your own DPC practice? Then let's do this.

UPDATE: The freedom is real. The control is real. The better income is real. And the world is starting to catch on. More and more doctors are interested in Direct Primary Care. You can be the doctor you dreamed of being. Here is the best part. As more

and more stories are being published in papers and online, it is becoming more and more "acceptable" and known by the lay public. This means the risk, though always there, is becoming less. The tide is rising and the boats are floating. Personally, I helped out a young physician in opening his own DPC practice 10 miles from me. My consult fee? Zero. I didn't need his money, and I wanted him to succeed. He did. And, if it helps the system, then even better.

2. Hold On, Do You Really Want to Do This?

I want to stop you to make you think. This is a big undertaking, and I am going to reiterate what I said in the introduction. Do you really want to do this? Here are some questions to motivate you:

- Are you tired of working for someone else?

- Are you tired of working so hard and making so little?

- Do you hate administrators and working for administrators?

- Do you actually want to feel complete in treating a patient?

- Do you want more time with patients?

- Do you want to see 8 patients a day versus 25?

- Do you want to like your job?

- Do you want to like your patients?

- Do you want to work for yourself and your patients and not for an insurance company or for the government?

This all sounds good, right? And it can happen. But do you really want the responsibility of your own practice? Do you have the entrepreneurial spirit to grind and be patient until you become successful? I do NOT think this is the path is for everyone. At least not now. Maybe in 10 years, with more acceptance of the DPC concept, many patients will want it and new family docs can just open up and their practices will easily fill. But that isn't happening now. Right now you have to have a bunch of skills and personality traits to make it on your own. And you are on your own. Here are some more questions:

- Can you live on no money for a period of time as you build up your practice?

- Can you sit around twiddling your thumbs for the first few months while there are large gaps in your schedule?

9

- Are you able to truly be a salesperson and pitch your product to patients, to the media and to anyone you meet?

- Are you able to gather at least $10K to start so you can buy equipment, pay rent/deposit, furniture, etc?

- Can you pound the pavement to talk to other business owners?

- Can you talk to the media to get an article on your new practice?

- Can you talk to friends and the community and get the word out?

If you can't do most, if not all of the above, then go back and work for the man. I once had a medical partner who had a huge following of patients. She was revered by them. All she had to do was start the process of starting her own DPC practice, but she couldn't and never will. Why? She could not handle the anxiety and risk. There is nothing wrong with that. If, however, you answered yes to all these questions, then I have the secret sauce waiting for you. Now let's get you into your very own DPC practice.

UPDATE: I think Direct Primary Care is being more accepted since I first wrote this. It may not take ten years, but we are still not where we need to be. The public is addicted to the current healthcare and health insurance model. It has to change. As per last chapter, the word is spreading. Do you still only need $10K to start? It depends on what you are looking for. I know some doctors who have bought buildings. That's going to cost more. Also, the location you pick may demand a higher price. The new doc who I helped open a place near me needed more than that $10K. My landlord did NOT charge me for a buildout in the space. The new doc, however, was charged $30K, which I thought was a lot but his area is much wealthier. That being said, you still have to review and do all those things I listed out in the bullet points above. You also need to hone your pitch, be confident, and never give up. You are playing the long game here.

3. Leaving an Employed Practice

If you're starting your practice while working for somebody else, which most of us are by this time, then the job of getting patients for your future DPC clinic is tough. Here is where you really want to look at your contract to see if you can actually go out like a little birdie and fly on your own. Why? Because hospitals don't want you to be independent. They want to control you and therefore have no other choice other than to hurt you if you attempt to escape. It happened to me once, and I was sued for it in the past. I went from one hospital to another hospital, and I lost a hundred thousand dollar lawsuit because of a noncompete clause that had no end date. Luckily, I already had a deal with the new hospital that they would pay that money if I lost. It really doesn't matter because I went from one frying pan to another frying pan by being employed by a bunch of administrative morons. Hence, that is why I am finally doing DPC. Going on your own, however, does not mean it's any easier and you may not have a hundred thousand dollars laying around so you really want to make sure that you don't have a noncomplete clause looming in your contract. If you are sure there isn't a noncompete clause, it doesn't guarantee you are in the clear. You still want to check your contract to see what you can or can't do as you try to recruit patients for your next practice.

It's Gathering Info Time

We live in the technology age. Everyone now has an email address, and luckily it rarely changes. Heck, even very elderly patients check their emails now and then. If you decide to leave your employed practice and are going to open a DPC practice locally, then I recommend you start gathering email addresses. This sounds easier than it is. You really cannot just go into patients' records or charts. Why? For one, this may be unethical if not illegal. How can the hospital tell? If you don't l know by now, everyone who goes into a chart leaves a trail or electronic fingerprints.

So what do you do? Well, there are a few things. Once you decide you are thinking about starting a local DPC clinic, then it becomes "gathering time". Tell your patients that you want to start a newsletter to give them information. This is not a lie as creating a DPC newsletter is critical as you start your real practice, but that is for later. Anyway, you may even want to try and convince your hospital employer that you want to do this (before you give your notice) and who knows, maybe you can collect all those addresses at one time and the IT guy can give it to you. You're lucky if this happens and you walk away with the email address list. Odds are, though, this will make them suspicious or your newsletter will have to be sent by the hospital and go through seven committees of approval. In other words, this will just reinforce why you are leaving them in the first place.

The other option is to literally ask all the patients (you like) for their email addresses as you see them over your last year. This doesn't sound like much, but if you see a hundred patients a week for 50 weeks or so, you can get a lot of names. I recommend you tell these patients that you're working on some special project such as a health newsletter that you want to send to them. After you make your announcement about going on your own to start your own DPC practice, you can tell them you are getting their email addresses to stay in touch with him after you leave. That is the truth. The key here is getting some information so that you can keep providing them with emails about your new practice after you start.

Do not send emails, however, until you actually leave your employed practice. Many of you will get antsy and want to convert patients. Don't do it. This may trigger an investigation by your hospital or get you walked out of the practice by security. It is not worth it. One of those patients will call administration to either complain or ask why you are leaving or whatever. It is doesn't matter. You will get called out by the administration.

Lastly, leave on good terms. I have been known to use the scorched earth policy, and that is not a good idea here. Most administrators are evil and have very little to do each day. Do not give them something to do like figuring a way to hurt you. They will try and they usually do it. This doesn't mean you need to tell them of yourplans. It is best to surprise them. Say you are sorry versus asking for permission. Then you just say, "I just want to practice medicine the way it supposed to be in a small practice. I am sure it won't effect you at all." Then go quietly into the night. And kick the shit out of them by being successful.

UPDATE: Let me reiterate: do not trust the hospital that employs you. I know this sounds negative but it's better to be safe than to be sorry. Don't make any mistakes. Play nice if you can but expect the worst. I hear stories all the time where hospitals are truly trying to make life terrible for docs who leave to jump into DPC. Why? Think about it. You are their worst nightmare. You are the light that shines on the darkness out there and exposes to others why it doesn't have to be that way. And many of these administrators are the Lords of Darkness.

4. Are You Abandoning Your Present Patients?

Wait, you're having some guilt, right? I mean, if you're converting from a regular practice, then aren't you abandoning patients? The answer is no. If your patients don't follow with you, then they are abandoning you because they don't feel you are worth $75 a month (or the rate you charge). Their cell phone is worth it. Their cable bill and gym memberships are worth it. But you are not.

I have heard this from two doctors personally. One runs an independent practice and figures he makes about $8 an hour because of how much time he has to work, and how little he gets paid. He has a large Medicare population, and they all are ill with multiple complaints. They eat up all his time on each visit, and he is getting paid less and less from the government. He is worried that he would be jettisoning them if he converts to a DPC practice. My response is that they would be jettisoning him. God love the "greatest generation", but in my experience these people will not pay a dime more than what they feel they did by paying in the system; that being Medicare. Forget that fact that they are inaccurate and the system is paying much more than they paid in. Forget that fact that they are paying very little now, as compared to the rest of us. And forget the fact that they are the highest and most expensive utilizers of the healthcare system. Lastly, forget the fact that these patients really need the 30-60 min of time DPC gives them. The bottom line is that they are not going to pay the $75 because they are on a fixed income, whatever that excuse means. It certainly doesn't mean not going on cruises, playing golf, going out to dinner regularly, etc. I tried to tell my colleague that he will not keep these patients anyway, but he stated he needed to know that this is their decision and that he didn't do anything wrong. He welcomed them all to stay. They won't. He'll still feel guilty.

Another doctor states she has almost 7000 patients. I am not sure if that is true or not but that is what the administration for her large group practice told her. She feels terribly that she would be abandoning so many of these people. My answer is hogwash. First of all, only about 10% of her patients would convert to her new DPC practice. Once, again that is their choice and should show us all how much patients truly value us. I will explain later how there truly are needy people that can't afford our help, and how we can give that care away. For the rest, $75 a month is not breaking anyone's bank. Back to this female doctor. She told me she feels too bad about leaving these patients. She makes no mention that her current job makes her cry after work almost every day. She is miserable, overworked, overstressed and has lost years of time with her family. For what? She gets underpaid in her current situation, and if she died tomorrow her patients would be sad for a week and then move on to the next doc. I have seen it over and over again. Yes, even the death scenario I just described. Also, she has to decide whether she would rather give great care to 700 patients or crappy care to 7000 because that is the only kind of care a doctor can give to that many patients.

So let's say I convince her to go into DPC and finally find happiness in medicine again. If she truly had 7000 patients, she may be able to fill in day one. The truth of the matter is she won't. The large group, where she is a partner, would NEVER let her contact these patients in a way to convert them. It turns out that she doesn't own them or their information. Also, those 7000 patients are probably not real and the number is inflated and false. If she converts, she may get 200 patients, and then she will have to start the grind like the rest of us. But it would be a different grind. She would be happy and enjoy seeing her patients and would stop crying every day after work. She would smile. What about the 6800 who didn't join? I am absolutely sure the large group she left would hire a doc quickly, if they found one, or hire two NPs or PAs. And her patients? They would move on or would follow her. The important point is, though, that it is their choice.

So let go of the guilt. You never became a doctor to be a pawn in some administrator's chess set. You wanted to see patients and help them. You wanted to give them great care, but the system won't let you do that. With DPC, you can and if people truly value you and their health, then they can have that care. If they TRULY can'tafford it, then give a certain percentage of your care away for free. I did this and gave away approximately 10%. I did not advertise this though. I felt good about it, and no one could accuse me of greed. What am I talking about? See the next chapter.

UPDATE: I found an interesting article in Medical Economics by Steven Schimpff MD on this same issue. The article was called *Direct primary care does not equate to patient abandonment* and was published in June of 2018. He said: "Yes, if lots of PCPs in one community converted all at once there could be a serious shortage. But that is not likely to happen. More likely is a gradual conversion process by those who wish to do so. It is not so unlike the PCP who quits his or her practice and seeks employment elsewhere. The affected patients will be cared for by other doctors in the communit who still do "production line medicine." And also said this, "The alternative is to wait and let the doctor totally burn out and close his or her practice; then no one gets the benefit of that physician."

5. Moral and Ethical Obligation

I once did a lecture at the University of Virginia on Direct Primary Care and was asked an interesting question. The attendee, who was an older doc, tried to put me on the spot with this rant:

"If all primary care doctors were to go into DPC, who would take care of the patients that couldn't afford it? Don't you think you have a moral and ethical obligation to take care of all patients?"

Ah, the old guilt trip. The first thing I said is that if all family doctors went into DPC, then maybe medical students would see the light and go that route as well. Who wouldn't want to make $240K plus a year and be the complete doctor they always wanted to be? The way the system is set up now there are few medical students wanting to go into FP and there is a major shortage. This is why the creation of physician extenders (NPs, PAs) occurred. So, here is an idea. Maybe as FPs start to move into DPC, and this would not be fast, then the desire to go into family medicine would increase?

Second, I give away 10% of care away for free. It isn't a major problem for me, and I feel good about it. It turns out that a lot of DPC docs I know do the same thing? Why? Because they are human. If all DPC docs give 10% of care away, then we would make a big dent in the supposed lack of coverage of patients.

Third, affording a $75 month fee is different than choosing not to pay it. There are plenty of patients that this doc is trying to speak for who just choose not to pay my fee. That is fine, and it is their choice but that is all it is, a choice. They choose to get cable, high data smartphones, and on and on. That isn't a judgment. That's a fact. For the ones who truly cannot afford that, then we have other options. There is the free care that I, and other, DPC docs give. There are the federally qualified health centers. Oh, and all those NPs and PAs, that the government is pushing to take over primary care can now have the non-DPC patients. That would work for me and the patients have full choice again. They have a safety net of extenders or they can pay a monthly fee. You get what you pay for.

Lastly, I want to reverse the question on this bitter doctor from the conference. Is it moral and ethical for family doctors to be the pawns of hospital administrators? To be paid the lowest on the doctor scale? I can't remember taking the vow of poverty when I graduated medical school. Is it moral and ethical to see patients for seven minutes because the system as it is leaves you no choice? I can make the case that is immoral and unethical! Is it moral and ethical to give patients' data away to insurers, the government and whomever else and not know where it is going? I could go on and on.

I asked a group of DPC docs for their thoughts on this and here are their answers:

For that same argument, that old doctor should never be able to retire. Because by his logic it would be immoral of him to ever stop and take time for himself. As long as there are patients to be cared for, there should be doctors missing their families to care for them. I would make an argument that he has more of the responsibility than the rest of us. He's older, which means all of his bills are paid off, which means he can work for free. He's living off Medicare and he probably made a ton of money during the 80s when medicine was profitable. He's probably one of the docs who sold us down the river and made it bad."

What happens when a doctor becomes an administrator and doesn't care for anyone? No one bats a freaking eye. I actually got into this argument with the family doctor who just became the chief medical officer of our local ACO. What do plumbers do for people who can't afford their services? Do they have a moral obligation to work for free? Clean waters been documented to be more helpful than most things."

"There is good data supporting the lower costs and better outcomes with quality primary care. Given that, if third party payment were part of a research trial it would've been stopped years ago as the effect of insurance on primary care is unethical."

"The goal is to expand the pie, not shrink it. You might have thanked the retired doc and his generation of physicians for allowing this mess to have happened in the first place. Had they not been seduced by all the third party payments, which were very generous initially (including Medicare and Medicaid), we would not be struggling to fix the dysfunctional system. He probably practiced in a time when reimbursements were great and paperwork minimal. Back then, almost all doctors were rich. The problem is that stereotype no longer fits reality (unless you are an administrator, cardiologist, radiologist, etc.) The drug dealer gives you the first few vials of crack for free. Once you are hooked, he owns you."

"It is interesting that they often completely ignore the otherwise monumental things DPC doctors done to lower medications and labs by 95%!! That helps the poor people everyday!"

"The more I get this question, the more it makes me irate. And here's fundamentally why. Risk- averse docs are pissed that people are untethering themselves from what they 'should do' and paving a path that returns some of the integrity and intangible reward to this profession. And so they're grabbing for evidence of why this model is corrupt. If you've spent your whole career gutting it out because "this is the way it is" it probably sucks to realize you could have done things another way. Fundamentally, however, the data is overwhelming. What we have is not working. It doesn't work for patients OR the physicians. Is the plan to take the population of the U.S., divide it by the number of physicians and that's our "quota"? This question, put in mathematical terms, makes NO sense. We all seem to agree that a teacher, who sees her "clients" EVERY day, can barely manage a 1:24 ratio... So 1:3000? 1:5000? Where does it stop?

I would also add that the personal and social cost for me to become a physician to then be doing 30% or more of unneeded administrative crap, leave medicine at age 45 or commit suicide... none of this benefits society either. The math that people use to imply I'm not pulling weight is garbage."

"My Answer: No! And then ask him: Why? That question is never adequately answered. Why do doctors, uniquely among all professions, not have the same moral right to their own lives, their own livelihoods, and to set the terms of their relationships with customers? I think we have to address this issue head on. The premise of that question, that health care is a right, is THE ESSENTIAL PROBLEM medicine faces today. All practical arguments are fine, but ultimately we have to assert our MORAL RIGHT to our own life, liberty and the pursuit of happiness. We have to assert our MORAL RIGHT to freely and independently contract for our own services, on our own terms just like every other profession."

"My argument for the question "this will worsen the physician shortage" is that there is no physician shortage. I challenge students all the time to answer this question. If you look at a study done by the American Academy of family physicians, 22% of our time is wasted on non-clinical paperwork. And yes, we all know that and the insurance-based doctor spends a lot more than 22% of their time on insurance paperwork. But that 22% of the time multiplied across the physician workforce would give us the equivalent of 168,000 full- time equivalent physicians, essentially overnight. They're only projecting the shortage of family physicians to be between 50 and 130,000 x 2025. So we don't have a shortage of physicians. We have an efficiency issue. DPC fixes that issue.

By the way, when I gave my answer to this older doctor, he didn't care respond. fixes that Maybe efficiency even more issue." interesting is that no one else came to his defense. That doesn't mean he was alone because I know there are others out there, and they have what I call Death Row Syndrome. I will explain that later.

6. Cherry Picking?

There is concern that DPC clinics cherry pick healthier patients. In fact, that is kind of what that doctor from the last chapter was insinuating when he questioned my moral and ethical obligation. So are we cherry picking patients? No, but there is some grain of truth in there. We just need to look at all sides of the issue here. The government and the naysayers are going to try and stop the Direct Primary Care trend. A recent CNN article spoke highly of our model but they allowed some idiot, who is the director of health policy at the consumer advocacy group Families U.S.A., to give her two cents. Kathleen Stoll fears that doctors who switch to a cash-only model "will drive away the patients who can't afford a monthly membership fee or thousands of dollars for an operation."

"They cherry-pick among their patient population to serve only the wealthier ones," Stoll said. "It certainly creates a barrier to care."

She's also concerned that the limited scope of the discounts these doctors negotiate for services outside their purview may not cut it if a patient comes down with a really serious illness.

"I'm always cautious when it's a cash basis," she said. "Are you somehow being put at risk? I'd have a list of questions."

My question to you and to her is, how does $75 monthly drive away people? How does this put people at risk? They (government, insurance carriers, etc.) are threatened and so they are trying to create doubts in public's mind. This is propaganda.

The truth of the matter is that people are paying much more per year out-o-pocket to their family docs when they have a high deductible insurance. With a DPC practice, their cost is at least a known quantity. As docs try to grow their practices, it may seem that patients who are more health conscious and proactive may be the first to join. That is the cherry picking. That isn't the doctor's fault.

I try to promote the fact that my office may save you money in the long run, but if the public is not getting it or decides not to go to the doctor's office anymore then it isn't my fault.

Don't get stuck in this argument. You offer treatment for 80-90% of all healthcare problems at a $75 month rate. Any one and every one is welcome. The very poor have Medicaid. The very rich have concierge care. The elderly have Medicare. The rest can decide if $75 a month is worth paying for personal, accessible and comprehensive care. Then, they can be the first cherries picked.

UPDATE: Many of my DPC colleagues revel in sharing our "cherry picking" cases on Facebook. The number of patients with very difficult issues who get fixed due to incredible care continues to grow. I am continually amazed at the work my peers are doing. Sure, I have had some tough cases as well, but what I see other DPC docs doing out there continues to boggle my mind. I am so proud of them. The "cherry picking" argument is actually asinine.

7. If You Are a Resident

I once did a talk for a family practice residency. I changed my talk so it was applicable to them. For example, I didn't really talk about which EMR system to buy or how find an office, etc. Why? I soon realized that they knew NOTHING about Direct Primary Care. NOTHING! So, I went in another direction. I started by breaking down how we are devalued as family docs. How administrators are multiplying faster than rabbits on Viagra. How we are pawns in the machine, only to be replaced by NP/PAs. I explained that DPC gives control back to their lives. I showed how easy it is to start a practice, but that it may take time to build it up. I told them how much money I make and how few patients I see a day. Their response? About 90% had their eyes glazed over.

So what was happening here? I am not totally sure. It was in January so many of the third years had already signed somewhere. They are also in residency mode and I tried to put myself in their shoes. They have to go to these weekly lectures. They just want to graduate or get through their rotations and can worry about their future in the future. I kept this in perspective. I asked how many were interested, after I was done with my talk, in doing DPC. About 6 of them raised their hands. I then asked only the ones who didn't raise their hands, why not? No one would answer. They just stared at me. It was weird. Then one dude, who was actually chief resident, stated a few interesting points for feedback:

- He was worried that this concept is still new and who knows if it will stand the test of time.

- He was worried about not having the resource or capital to start this right out of residency.

- He thinks that it takes a lot of balls to do this and not every resident has the courage to risk this.

- Shouldn't residents take some time to see patients in a bigger practice or system before opening up their own place in order to gain experience?

I think this resident's points were valid. I don't think they are complete though. First, to his points. As far as the newness, I get it. The only thing new, however, is that people pay monthly instead of per visit. That was the old way and has been around since Hippocrates. The system is so perverted now that residents cannot fathom a world without insurance companies. The resident fears that the AAFP, the AMA, the government or the insurers will work to shut us down. I tried to reassure him that DPC is actually in the ACA, but he does have a point. If all doctors jump, then the idiots with power will try to hurt us. That is a risk. How? I am not sure but I don't trust them. Absolute power corrupts absolutely and that is what the corrupt healthcare industry has been doing for years.

His second issue of capital is questionable. It takes less than $20K to start up a DPC practice that is well equipped. You also are making little money in the beginning. This is tough but residents should be used to it. In reality, they are just tired of being broke and don't want to suffer for a few more years. I get it. They think, however, that by working for the man for a few years they will then convert to a DPC? Wrong. What happens is you get used to the money. Like a stripper who can't get off the pole, family doctors have bills and they and their families get used to a lifestyle and then you are stuck. Forever.

His third issue is real to an extent. Yes, it does take courage to think out of the box, and then act on it. I am disturbed that the faculty makes no mention of DPC. I am disturbed that the AAFP doesn't point this out to residents enough. The doctors of yesteryear had no problem with putting up their own shingle and starting business. I think what he was really worried about is getting patients to buy in and join. That is realistic. The truth is, residents are trying to find themselves and be confident in their skills and don't want to worry about pitching and finding patients. This leads to my last point.

24

I do think residents should get as much experience as possible and that comes with volume so you can see more and more symptoms, diseases and problems. A resident could do this even with opening up a DPC practice. She would just have to moonlight at an urgent care on the weekends. I would not recommend taking any Medicare or Medicaid patients in the DPC practice until you are making it and can stop moonlighting. So, at first I would not opt-out of Medicare/Medicaid. You just would not take those patients in your first DPC year. I recommend busting your ass for 12 hours on Saturday and Sunday because you will be twiddling your thumbs during the week. That way you are making money and gaining that experience. The other option is to work for the man for a few years with a definite, but secret, DPC plan that you lock into. Tell no one. Gain your experience. And then definitely stick to your plan no matter what. And don't sign a noncompete clause if at all possible!

So what have we learned here? My talk was for residents, but they were clueless. It is going to take time for the world of family medicine to understand DPC. Maybe my talk helped push a few in that direction. Maybe not. The bottom line is that even with all their excuses, it doesn't change a thing. They can become the doctors they always wanted to be if they want it bad enough. End of story. Instead, half of the graduating class told me they are becoming hospitalists. Wow. How pathetic. They went into family medicine so they don't have to do family medicine?

Sometimes things that seem too good to be true are actually true.

Update: DPC is not "new" anymore. I don't love the AAFP, but they do put on the DPC Summit and there are DPC lectures at their yearly AAFP FMX conference. I know ALL the people doing those lectures and they are great representatives for DPC. The word is spreading more and more so that even the residents and medical students at least know about this. The courage, the upfront money and the experience is still the same. More and more residents are doing DPC right out of the gate, and I think that is awesome. The issue of big organizations (hospitals, insurers, government, etc.) trying to stop DPC is always a small risk, but that risk gets smaller as we get more powerful and larger in numbers.

The DPC Alliance has now formed as the only organization truly representing DPC. Please join them! Also, politicians are on our side because we are cheap, save money and patients love us. This does not mean we don't have to worry, but right now DPC is in the right lane.

SECTION TWO

Okay, You Decided to Make
the Leap

1. Okay, How Do I Get Started?

First, make the decision that you are all in.

Second, commit to a date and do not push that date out too far. Make it three months at the longest. Give yourself some motivation. Time will do that.

Third, start doing some research. This book is part of that. I tried to ask a lot of the first pioneers their thoughts on all these chapters. I included what I thought was important, but this should not stop you from digging deeper.

Here are some resources that I recommend you check out:

- Podcasts on DPC – There are a few. Heck, I have been interviewed on a few. Some are defunct now but they are still good. Podcasts are great to listen to in the car to learn as many little tricks as you can on getting patients and making your practice great.

- Podcasts not related to your field but still pump you up and teach you things. For example, the Tim Ferriss Show or ones on marketing like Online Marketing Made Easy. Explore others as more are added each day.

- Articles on Direct Primary Care – Google, Google, Google. Read DPCNews.com, which is a site I started to coordinate and collect all this material.

- Books on Business – I recommend the following:
    - Small Giants
    - The Starbucks' Experience
    - Everything is Marketing
    - The 1 Page Marketing Plan
- Conferences

- AAFP FX, which has DPC lectures
- DPC Summit
- HINT Summit

- Atlas MD – yes, the EMR company has a good resource page to start your DPC practice.

- The DPC Alliance – I helped found this organization to be a voice for DPC, but it also has a reservoir of great information. Please join. There is tons of stuff there for you to learn.
- Facebook – I hate Facebook but the DPC Docs (spelled exactly that way) page continues to grow and there is great support there. You have to be added and prove you are a doctor. I highly recommend it.

- Network (more on this later)

I recommend keeping a journal from the day you start and keeping it going forever. To be honest, *The Direct Primary Care Doctor's Daily Motivational Journal* can be a useful tool to get you started or just use a notebook to record your thoughts. A journal is critical to reinforce what works and what doesn't work. It will also get you motivated every day and help you focus. It will make you feel that you accomplished things even you had a bad week. So, here is what I recommend you write in your journal, but feel free to change it to fit your needs:

- What do I need to accomplish today to feel good about myself?

- What can I do to make my office experience better?

- What marketing techniques can I try?

- What has worked well today in the office?

- Who can I call today to help me reach my goals?

- Are there any broken windows in the practice?

- What have I learned from a book that relates to my DPC practice?

- What have I accomplished this week in the practice?

- How many active patients do I have now?

- How can I be a better doctor for my patients?

These are just some of the things I use. I also find a quote from someone famous and put it up top of each entry. I am a big believer in reading and finding ideas that can relate to my practice. This not only includes books but also magazines like Entrepreneur or Inc.

You actually may need one motivation journal as noted above and another idea journal. That is what I did when I started. You are in a new world, my friends. You have to do everything on your own now, and though you will have people to call on to help, like me, it is still up to you. Learn. Try new things. Put on your big person pants. It is time to grow up and shock the world by succeeding where the administrators said you couldn't.

*Odds are you will blow off this journal idea, but I would recommend you think twice about that. You are heading for some great days and some dark days. It's easy to get through the great days. It's the dark days that will scare you. Trust me. So keep a log, keep the motivation up and use all your tools to keep pushing the boulder up the hill. It helps a lot.

Update: This list is not all inclusive. DPC keeps changing. What won't change is your need to keep optimistic in the face of what seems like failure. The resources and journal will help you do that. Just fifteen minutes each morning with DPC-specific questions will help you be the doctor you always wanted to be, in the practice you always wanted to have. But there's a secret: you can't be told what to think or believe. You must work through the process and find the answers yourself. That is what this book is for.

2. The Basics

Ok, so you have gathered the most information you can, and you are really going to do this. You may have a list of patient emails. You have read everything you can think of. You started a journal. Now you have to get some basics down. These are not all-inclusive and this list will get bigger as we go.

- Pick a name - I would put Direct Primary Care in there but that is up to you. Names are important and you are stuck with it once you start. Do you want your last name in there? That may a great branding idea but what if you sell it? It was easier for me when I sold mine because my practice had the name of my town, not my name, in it.

- Colors - This is important. Each color has significance and some feel wrong for what we do. Red is for emergency, for example. Take your time on this one.

- Logos - Don't do this on your own. Get a local group to make one for you and be intimately involved in the process. You may want to research ideas on how to come up with a logo on the internet. The more info you give the graphic designer, the easier it will be for her, and the more you will like the outcome. It may even be cheaper. Crowdsourcing on sites such as DesignCrowd worked for me, but getting someone local may end up getting you patients as that person talks to new clients all the time.

- Build a website - You can do this on your own with Wordpress. I did it myself, but you don't have to. There are plenty of crowdsourcing companies that will make you a deal. You will need your logo done for this. My EMR, described later, works within my website so patients can sign up right there. See www.forestdpc.com

- Set up your social media accounts (Facebook, Twitter, Instagram, etc.)

- Set up a Google business account.

31

- Business Cards - For you and your staff members. You can do this on your own, I believe, on Vistaprint since you already have the logo.
- Brochures - You can go on Vistaprint and do this but I am not sure that comes out as well. My staff and I decided on the information we wanted in the brochure, and then we used DesignCrowd to hire a designer for my brochures. This will be talked about later. We had a dozen great designers, just like with the logo, who submitted their ideas. We then took some from each and worked with one designer and made a brochure. We used that guy again for my college brochure and it cost about $100.
- Get an accountant - I formed a PC or professional corporation (Sub S). You may want to do the same but ask your accountant. I use Quickbooks to do my own books and then send the information to my accountant. She takes care of the government taxes, like payroll, and tells us what to pay my assistant/phlebotomist. This costs me about $150 – 200 a month. Funny, isn't it? That is at least twice what I charge for a membership, and I am supposed to feel guilty. My accountant doesn't and I don't blame her.
- Get a lawyer to register your corporation and do the legal mumbo jumbo that you need to have done.
- Get a bank account and make sure you keep your account clean and specific to just your new office.
- Find an office.
- Get a phone number.
- Set up your internet and Wifi.
- Get an EMR.
- Hire one staff person.
- Get a fax service - We use Ring Central to digitize all faxes so I don't waste paper or have to convert those paper faxes to a

digital version on my own. It costs less than $100 a year and has met all our needs.

- Line up your utilities like water, electricity, heat, etc.

- Get quality printers but don't spend too much on them. I would suggest laser printers, with only one of them having color capability. Regular, non laser, printers run through a lot of ink and is not worth it in the long run.

- Get laptops for the office. I use an Apple. My wife and assistant tried Google Chromebooks at first. Later on, we all went to MacBooks.

- Set up your hazardous waste disposal - There are a lot of scammers out there who do this, and will keep trying to contact you. I would suggest a local, reputable company. You will NOT have that much waste. We pay pick up and, at most, need this done three or four times a year for a total of about $100 a year.

- Set up an OSHA manual and post the required notices. Have a basic hazardous waste kit.

- MEDICARE - If you are going to moonlight, while ramping up, then you really can't drop Medicare. You can either treat some Medicare patients for free or just not take them while you are still trying to make money on the side. You won't make that much money your first year in a DPC practice unless you get lucky or if you are taking over an established practice. At some point, the big decision you must make is whether you are going to opt out of Medicare or not. I did because I want nothing to do with government and its interference in my practice. You have to make a decision on this because the default is being opted in either individually or through your corporation. If you decide to opt out you must write a letter to Medicare telling them such. This can take up to 60 days. You can find a sample opt out letter on the AAPS website and just search sample Medicare opt out forms. If you still want to be able to make referrals on your Medicare patients, you need to fill out form CSM 8550. You can do these online but it can be a little tricky to figure it out. You also need to have your NPPE number and you should update your info online. Anything you send to the government about opting out must be sent certified mail with signature return. You also must then enter into a contracted agreement with your Medicare patients stating they know that you will not charge Medicare and they will not submit any bills to Medicare to pay for your services. If you do labs in your office, you can still bill Medicare. You will need to be aware of which labs Medicare will cover. You will need to do an ABN (Advanced Beneficiary Notice) for any lab not covered. We use LabCorp and they have an ABN tool right on its website.

- Get malpractice insurance – The company that I used was Norcal. They may be gone or have changed names as you read this. I highly recommend you ask around for companies doing DPC malpractice insurance. Ask the DPC Alliance if they have connections. Ask the DPC Docs FB page or search it. Get the cheapest one you can get, and it is cheap because of the lack of lawsuits in DPC due to the great relationships we have with our patients and the time we spend with them. Make sure, however, that you list EVERY procedure you do, or may do in the future, for the insurance company. Read the fine print. Do not get burned doing vasectomies and the malpractice company denying to cover you later on.

3. How Much Will You Be Charging and For What?

The concept behind Direct Primary Care is that it is a monthly fee. It is not a cash-based practice where you get paid for each visit or you will end up trying to fill the day like you used to. That is human nature. The monthly fee covers everything you do including their emails, texts, phone calls and obviously their visits. It also includes my newsletter and lectures. That is my package and I explain that to each patient. The only other fee is the registration fees, and anything that costs me will cost them. So, for example, if I have to buy their labs then they need to pay me back because I am buying it for them. It is highly discounted, though.

The Registration Fee

I think is important to have a registration fee. Pick a price but I charge the same as my monthly fee. This $80 is per person to a maximum of $160 for a family. Gyms do it. Golf clubs do it. You should do it. Do not devalue what you do. You can defer to my discussion about value, but the registration fee also locks them in for at least a month or more. Why? We've had times where patients have come and had their physicals done and then quit. In other words, they were just using us to get a cheap physical. I will tell you how to spot these people later, but be aware that this happens. By having the registration fee paid up front, which gets you a total of $160, you haven't lost any money.

The registration fee also is valid because you and/or your staff are doing work for this. You have to get the patients' old records, which includes time for faxing and getting in touch with those offices. You also to make sure that the information is right, their medications are recorded and so forth. Once again don't devalue yourself because this is your time. It is also another way to get money in the bank for your practice, and with 600 patients, this adds up to a good sum over the year.

This registration fee can also be discounted as an incentive. So, for example, let's say you are transitioning your regular practice over to a DPC. You want them to join soon so that you have cash flow coming in right way. One way is to give patients in your current practice a deadline of a month to sign up for the new practice and waive the registration fee if they do it.

Lab Fees

I charge patients for their labs if they don't use their insurance because I buy it for them from LabCorp, and they simultaneously pay me back. We rounded those fees up from LabCorp to me, and therefore make a little money on each patient but not much. This is a bargain for patients and should be used to market how they are saving money. If it is a patient who truly likes to "biohack" and check how their labs have changed with their lifestyle changes, then all the better.

Pathology Fees

We found a place in North Dakota who would pay for the FedEx of pathology specimens (mole removals, biopsies, etc.) and the cost was $75 total. My local pathologist came to my office to pitch their services. It was $175 per specimen. I told them of this other competitor out of state. Result? It is now $75 here in town and I use the local group. Don't you just love the free market? The only other pathology fee is a Pap smear at $35.

Monthly Fee

Everybody seems to have a little different number, but I highly recommend you do NOT sell yourself cheap or sell yourself short. You are worthy of at least what I charge which is $80 a month for an individual, $135 for a couple and $165 a month for an entire family (up to age 21). For that family deal, we allow no more than 5 people. Any more than that, then it is $10 more per person, per month. You can tweak these numbers if you want, but I came up with them by doing an intense internet search of other DPC docs and averaging the numbers out. Others also do it a little differently. For example, Josh at Atlas.MD uses age as a way to tier prices. It is up to you.

Copays

Some people charge copays for their visits. I do not. You want patients to come in. You want to make this system simple. Don't nickel and dime people. It turns patients off.

Hybrid Practices

They fail. In fact, they are the few DPC ventures that do fail. You cannot do two things in one practice and not expect patients to be confused, angered or jealous. In a hybrid model, you do not get the true DPC experience. There is still a waiting room of sick patients. Patients are not the only person in the office at the time of your visit. In a hybrid model, you often have a larger staff since the number of patients is higher and because you are running two different models. The only competition we ever had was jerk trying to undercut my prices pretending to be a DPC practice. He was a hybrid and hardly even. He had 10 staff members and no special treatment for his DPC patients. What a joke. Trust me, this hybrid model practice soon becomes very similar to the industrialized fee-for-service model.

Let go of the insurance model. You cannot be half pregnant.

Urgent Care Visits

They work great for your own patients. Don't offer this to non-patients or all your regular patients will become non-patients. Capisce?

Meds

Some practices offer very cheap prescription drugs. This is about offering more value to their patients. I get that. It didn't seem workable for me due to the effort and state regulations of Virginia. I think it is worth a look into, however, for you. I have heard great stories on how it works, but I also have heard horror stories about the amount of effort it takes. Ask others.

Other Services

Some DPC docs charge extra for home visits. Some offer extra services like counseling, massage, yoga, etc. These are great ideas and you need to decide what works for you. I am one of the rare MDs that does OMT or osteopathic manipulative therapy. Those treatments are normally $100-$150, but they are free to my patients.

Update: After four years, I raised my prices a bit. When the book first came out it was $75 a month. I also allowed unlimited family members for one prices. I changed because I had a family of 11 wanting to join and realized that I was getting ripped off at this price. I honored the old price and held my breath. They still didn't join. This should tell you how much people don't value us at times.

4. Medical Records

You obviously have to keep some records for patient care and for medical-legal issues (in case you get sued). Hopefully, the latter will never happen. You also want your patient care to be complete so that someone who's reading it the next time, which is probably you, can just follow the thread and enable you or him or her to give better care each time. That is something electronic medical records, as built for billing, does not do or care about.

I am not against EMRs (electronic medical records). The key is that it has to work for me and not some third party. To be fair to these EMR companies, that will never work if all the doctor is trying to do is massage the note in order to optimize his payment. In other words, as long as the doctor is working for the government or insurance company, a perfect EMR will not exist.

I use an EMR because I do want access to my records at home as well from the office. I also want my staff to easily access it even if I have the chart. This does not mean you can't use paper record charts, but I have moved my stuff to the cloud.

You can pick any electronic medical record system you want because it's up to you how much you want to pay. Some of them are free, and some of them are ridiculously expensive. You do get what you pay for, in my humble opinion, so buyer beware.

Personally, I used the Atlas.MD EMR system because I think it really was created for Direct Primary Care from the start. Josh Umbehr M.D. is at the forefront of this system and he does sell the software as well as champion the cause of Direct Primary Care. The system is built so that it does not only the recordkeeping but also does the billing piece. You must have some way to bill patients and you do not want to get into the cash or check or "I will pay you later" game. The Atlas. MD EMR does that part and helps in transferring those charges into your account. You would need to purchase an independent billing program if you don't use Atlas.MD. I liked using Atlas.MD because it tells you when people have not paid, and then you can track them down. And track them down I will. The cost for each transaction is a nominal fee, which is standard in every merchant business. I believe the monthly charge for the atlas EMR is more than reasonable. There will be a monthly fee for you and at the time of this writing it is $300 a month. Josh and his team give incredible customer service and get back to you right away.

Your office should have some sort of scheduling system. You can use paper but it is important to be efficient and effective. Most EMRs do that. You should also be able to track health maintenance issues because I think that is important as well. The rest of your EMR should be the way you want to build it. In other words, my notes are old-fashioned SOAP notes. It's old-school medicine once again that worked before and will work in the future. I initially used SimpleNote, which automatically updated on my Mac as well. Then I just pasted it in. I could have bought one of those Dragon Dictation systems but the cost is ridiculous. Later on my MacBook had an improved dictation option so I just used that.

I like the "story" of my patient encounters and not the box-clicking crap of most other EMRs. My notes are throwbacks to the old days, but what brings this Atlas.MD EMR into the 21st-century is its ability to email patients as well as text them. It also allows me to send email updates to patients. The system also notifies them a week prior as well the day prior that they have their appointments coming up so we do not have staff calling patients and reminding them. It even sends out Happy Birthday wishes. This has worked out really well for me. In summary, you can choose any EMR you want, but I think it should be made for DPC, made for you, have some special bells and whistles, be able to bill and collect from patients and be reasonable in cost.

Update: There ARE other companies out there vying to be the DPC EMR. Some have come and gone. I was always happy as a clam using Atlas.MD. I don't want to disparage other EMRs, though. I have heard great things about HINT. Test them all out.
Last tip: you may think you want expensive bells and whistles, but you don't need them.

5. Hiring the Right Staff

Hiring the right staff person is critical. How many staff you choose is obviously up to you, but you must realize that the bloated staff in the regular insurance model of healthcare delivery is not needed. They are there only to help satisfy useless metrics and to band-aid situations that are created by churning through too many patients. Happily, these scenarios no longer apply to you in your DPC practice. Your job is to help patients, give them satisfying experiences and make sure they spread the word about you. In my opinion, you need only ONE really good staff person. That being said, I also have my wife help as the practice manager a few hours each day.

Finding that one great staff person is not always that easy. If you are in a private practice model already and want to convert to a DPC practice then you have some hard choices to make. Do not feel guilty about letting staff go. Retain your best person and move on. This is business. Keeping your staff so they can sit around all day twiddling their thumbs will only piss you off and make you go broke. Remember, you are taking a huge risk going into a DPC practice. Make it a calculated risk and make your office lean. This may also mean keeping a really good staff person at a lower price versus keeping the star RN at higher price. It's your money and you want to make this work. Be smart.

That being said, here are some other things for you to think about:

What is the job?

I needed someone to take blood from kids to adults. That was critical to me. An MA would work if she had a lot of experience doing this. A phlebotomist would also work if she wasd malleable and could learn to answer the phones, do vital signs, be my assistant and such.

Will you be drawing labs at your office?

I recommend you do because you can save patients a lot of money while even making a little bit yourself. It is also good service to draw blood right in your office and a great marketing advantage.

How much do you want to pay?

You probably will never have the volume to need an RN who costs a lot of money. In my area, the sweet spot was around $13 an hour, and I found a great phlebotomist with a full four-year college degree who was willing to learn. She now runs the place.

Do they have baggage?

Check everything you can about your interviewees. Read their Facebook. Read their Twitter. Read their blogs. Google their names. Call their references. I eliminated a lot of candidates this way.

How much to advertise for staff?

When I worked in an urgent care I kept seeing staff searching on a site called Indeed.com. When I decided to open my practice, I found this site affordable and I received hundreds of submissions of resumes. You can use any site you want, but this was very cheap. Do not pay a lot!

Interview the person a few times and in different environments. Once in the office and once at a coffee shop, for example. People are different when they let their hair down, which can be good or bad.

I have heard the saying, "Hire slow, fire fast" and I believe it. Take your time in hiring because you never know what is hidden in these candidates' closets. This staff person is your major connection to your patients. If they suck, you suck. So, remember, if they turn out bad right away then fire them right away. You have too much to do and don't need another project.

Make sure they have a bubbly personality.

People come in to your office and don't want to see a moody staff person. Patients are sick and need to see a smile when they walk in.

Are you compatible with this person?

There has to be chemistry with the person you are hiring. Make sure you have a list of important questions to understand their point of view on things. For example, do they understand the concept of DPC. If the person did not even take time to research it before interview, then she is a no go. It is the easiest test to see if they are someone who will go the extra mile to get the job. There never is a traffic jam on the extra mile.

Do not ask questions that are inappropriate or illegal. Look this up online. For example, how old are you or what religion do you practice amongst others are illegal questions to ask of a job candidate.

This was my ad:

"Medical Assistant/Phlebotomist: New type of practice needs MA with great phlebotomy and personal skills. Must be positive/happy person and an enthusiastic learner. This is a low volume FP clinic with a high caring attitude. No more churning through patients! Personal interest in exercise/alternative medicine a major plus. www.forestdpc.com"

There is no magical formula for getting a great staff person. Remember, take your time and don't wing it. This position is too important.

Update: The same staff person was with me until I retired. She was a phlebotomist who I trained to do everything else. She was wonderful and stayed with the new doctor when he took over. The only time we had to use someone else is when she went on maternity leave. We thought we did everything right to hire someone for this temporary period. It was a horror show. We fired that person and had to wing it until my permanent assistant returned. This stuff ain't easy.

6. Do you Still Need Midlevels like PAs and NPs?

The need for midlevels, like PAs and NPs, in DPC practices often comes up. The answer is that you probably don't need them. They were created, as what they were once called, to be physician extenders. In other words, doctors had so many patients that they needed to use some other professional to extend their reach. Well, with DPC, you have only around 600 patients, so why would you need that extension anymore? You don't. I guess if you could not find a partner and you were filled, then you could consider hiring a midlevel. You could pay him a salary or take a percentage of his monthly fees by patients, but this gets confusing. If someone is a patient of the NP but wants to see a doctor for a bigger issue do you let them? And who wants to have an NP when they can have a MD or DO? I am trying not to make this political, but our extra years of training and countless hours in residency counts for something. The bottom line is that patients will pick you over the NP or PA. If your NP or PA is only seeing acutes, then you are not doing the job you told patients you would be doing. Do you see how this gets to be problematic? At this time, and unless I see working examples otherwise, then I see no reason to have an NP or PA. They can have the jobs we left at the hospitals.

This is my opinion, obviously. I have a really good friend who is a PA and would love to work with her, but I cannot see how it fits with my DPC practice. I do know great DPC docs who use midlevels and it works out well for them. I have no qualms about this.

Now, let me point out a disturbing trending and it is called FPA (full-practice authority). I do NOT believe that NPs and PAs should be allowed to practice on their own. Their "studies" that they claim prove they are the "same or better" than doctors are poorly designed and even laughable. Competing with an NP and PA is not an issue as I believe doctors win out. Simply and importantly put, doctors have   much more training and education than midlevels. This is an easy sell. The problem becomes when midlevels cut our prices in half to compete against us. Remember that whole collaboration thing they sold to the world. Nope. Anyway, they can cut their prices because they are used to making a lower salary.

I am also bothered by midlevels calling themselves doctors because that is professional appropriation. They are only trying to confuse patients. This is very unsettling as we see more and more online diploma mills for NP and DNP degrees. The cases of malpractice against these specific and poorly trained midlevels is exploding. I would recommend you look up, and possibly support, the Physician for Patient Protection organization as well as read the book Patients At Risk.

Once again, this is NOT an attack on NPs or PAs. The reverse is actually happening. NPs and PAs are doxing doctors and destroying their patient rating sites if they speak up against this surge of poorly trained midlevels. Since when is it wrong to point out the differences in education and training between doctors and NPs/PAs? These are facts.

The bottom line is that I really hope that DPC practices have great doctors behind them. If they use a midlevel and supervise them closely, then great for them. I do not support poorly trained and poorly educated NPs or PAs trying to get FPA. I am afraid of them poisoning the good name of DPC, especially if they are doing harm.

7. Setting Up the Physical Office

If you build it, they will come is the famous line from Field of Dreams. That sounds great but it is NOT true. First, I don't recommend you build anything. Unless you are independently wealthy, that is a huge investment you don't need right away. My rent was initially $1400 a month for about 1500 square feet. This went up to about $1700 a month over six years. This totally depends on what state you live in and what part of town you want to place your office. The next question should be do you need an office at all? I believe you do. A physical office gives patients comfort and the DPC concept is hard enough already for them to grasp. Having no "home" office may just be too much to handle. This is not to say that it can't be done. I know of a doctor who came out of residency, Dustin Clark MD, and just started doing DPC without an office and he went to his patients' homes. I think that is great, but it is harder to do in the long run. Here are his thoughts:

"I did start a mobile DPC at first. I did so to save money and keep overhead low. It worked perfectly fine. The only negative was the driving distance and the difficulty with some procedures not traveling well. I switched to offering an office to attempt to grow the practice faster."

So, you have decided to rent a place. Where? The mantra has always been location, location, location, but that may not totally be true for DPC practices. You are not an urgent care center and you don't want people popping in to be seen that day only to find out you are a membership model practice and don't take insurance. Sure, it will be good to be on a busy street so potential customers will see you but it may not help to convert them to patients and you are paying a premium for this location. Eventually, in a year or two, you will be filled and don't need that prime and expensive location to recruit more patients. That being said, you need a nice office and one that has good parking, is big enough to feel good to the patient, and is in a nice area.

Here are some tips that we found helpful:

Decide how big of a place you want and the area you want to be in. Drive around and look and do research. You can get a commercial realtor, but I found they are often not that interested in finding low-priced rental properties for you...not enough gain for them. We found the place on our own by researching, talking to people, driving around and keeping our eyes and ears open. Try to stay lean...remember this will be one of your biggest beginning expenses. Talk with your realtor about what is included in the price, including such things as trash and plowing. Make sure you have enough storage space and shelves. You wind up using more than you think. Also try to get a staggered rent over three years. Note, most people don't want to give you a lease for less than a three- year commitment; especially if they have to do some remodeling for you. Our owner took out carpet, put in tile, added sinks, and painted. He also did a really good cleaning. Try to anticipate your needs so you can include this in the contract price.

Your owner will have insurance, but he may also require you to take additional coverage. Our business policy was about $300 a year and we have a 1500 square foot place. Make sure you have enough electrical receptacles and phone/internet connections. If not, try to work this into the deal also.

Gas is usually cheaper than electric or oil so check on this. Try to find out what it cost the previous renter before you decide on utilities. You can call each company. Also, be prepared to pay some considerable deposit fees. Columbia Gas alone charged us a $460 deposit fee. Work this into your budget. Shop for your phone/internet provider. You may be limited by what is available in your area. You will have to pay for a business internet/phone connection even if it is less than the level of service you may have for residential. They will know by your address, and they will come out. Shop around and ask for better prices. It can help. We initially paid $120 for Shentel for a three year commitment for phone and internet (business); about $40 more than our residential plan which has a higher speed internet connection...but it all depends on availability. This price went up to about $170 after our three-year promotion pricing ended. We had looked at some VOIP services for phone but decided against based on our needs. We do use Ring Central for fax-to-internet connection.

This works with our EMR. Shop around in the beginning, and then reevaluate over the years to make sure you are still getting the best deal.

Now that you have the place, you have to decide on your set up. Our office has one greeting area, a lab/omt room, one exam room, a handicap accessible bathroom, a reception/waiting area, a small kitchen and one doctor's office with a private bathroom. We also have two three-shelf storage closets. Lastly, we have rooms upstairs that we are not using at the present time.

Decide on your colors; perhaps coordinated with your logo. We had an idea of what we wanted for our logo and then we bid out for designs on. This is very reasonable and we had good results. We have one big canvas print of our logo done through one of the online canvas print companies. Look for a good sale and compare prices. We used Easy Canvas Prints. They also did some other prints of some photos for us. They did a good job.

Next, search your house for anything you can use the office. Use those items you might have boxed up in the attic. We finally had a place for all the old medical books and items we had been given over the years. We grouped them all into a hutch; which came from my dining room.

Search Goodwill and consignment stores. Look on Craigslist. We were able to buy an exam table, an EKG machine and many other supplies from a doctor who was retiring. We found great office desks also. We used a local moving company to move all this stuff. We were also able to buy a used chiropractic table, which was in great shape. For a crash cart, we bought a very sturdy rolling Craftsman tool cart. It matched our silver and black decor in our lab/OMT and it holds many supplies we need. We even have our EKG machine placed on the top of it. Search for you bargains! Keep it lean! Do not go overboard!

Enlist the help of a friend or relative who is good at interior design. My wife's stepmom saved us. She was able to pull an assorted group of items and turn them into a beautiful, coherent design. Your office speaks for your practice. Take some time to make it the place you want it to be. Include natural plants in the office. We were able to find some nice bargains and then found a lot of pots for transplanting at our local DAV store. We also used bookcases in the doctor's office and in reception area. We have a collection of rotating books for patients to look at and even to borrow (Just stamp the books with your name for easy return). We got these bookcases online. Wayfair and Overstock. com offer some good bargains. We got a nice L- shaped black table from Wayfair that we use for our blood draws.

Get a good laser-jet printer and perhaps a cheaper second printer. We don't have special office phones. We have just one line and three handsets. Calls can be transferred as need be. This has been very efficient and cost-effective. We don't need a phone attached to our fax because we use a fax-to internet service.

We have a small wireless speaker in the receptions area. We stream music from the phone, computer and now our Amazon Fire. An Amazon Echo speaker is a good option also. There is no TV for us.

Use lamps to provide an alternative to overhead, fluorescent lighting.

We have a 13 cubic refrigerator and microwave in the break room. We also have another smaller college dorm refrigerator for blood in one of our supply closets. We do not do vaccines so we do not need a big refrigerator.

We recently added a spring water (just cold water) cooler to our waiting room.

In conclusion, start with a good plan. Get some input if needed. Bargain shop. Create a welcoming environment. Modify as needed. It will feel so rewarding to come into an office that is warm and welcoming and is all yours! Enjoy.

8. Bartering

Remember the good old days when you could exchange an office visit for a chicken. Of course you don't because that was way before your time. The older family doctors paved the way for us in so many ways, some good and some bad, but one that really may help you out is called bartering. These docs did it because many patients could not afford care but these doctors didn't care and they did it for free. Most of these patients had pride and would do the doctor favors like giving him fresh eggs or cords of wood. Sometimes the doctor would make a deal. I will see your family for a year, and you can pave my driveway or fix my roof. These deals were easy to understand when you found out that the patient had a paving company or a roofing company. It was a way to get things done for the doctor as well as a way to help people out. Everyone was happy.

Nowadays, with so few independent doctors, no big corporations will barter with you. Hell, there is no suit who could make that decision anyway. All these idiots know is money, and can't see the big picture anyway so bartering has gone the way of the dodo. But it is back, and it starts with you!

First things first, you must check with your accountant about bartering. There are tax implications. If what you offer is way under the value of what you receive, then you could get a tax bill on the difference. That being said, it is still worth it. I have bartered with a local film company that makes business videos. I gave the owner free healthcare in my office for a year. I hired a marketing person who goes into offices to break the first barrier of entry so that I may speak to the person in charge. She gave me an hour or two a week ,and did things I don't like to do or just can't do. For that, I gave her a free year of healthcare for her and her family as well.

You can think of other things that may help you. Maybe your landlord could cut your rent for a membership? Do whatever works. If you don't have much money, then you have to do what you have to do. Except prostitution. Even I wouldn't do that. Yet. Do always check with your accountant if you have any questions or concerns about bartering.

9. Deliver an Experience

You have to understand that your patients need to brag about you. That is where word of mouth starts. They will brag about you if they have a positive experience in your office. If they leave happier than when they came in, you have truly left an impression in their minds. This is how you fill your practice. How hard is this to do? Well, fortunately, almost EVERY other regular medical practice doesn't care as much about the experience given to their patients so the bar is set really low. This doesn't mean it is easy, however, and you need to keep tabs on this constantly.

So, what is the experience you have created for your patients? It starts with your ads and business cards and logos. We went through that in previous chapters but I want to reiterate how important everything is to your patients. Now, go through everything else:

Look at your office from the outside:

How is the exterior of the building? Is it well maintained and clean?

How is the parking? This should never be a problem because you don't do a volume practice.

Is the area clean and landscaped well?

Is the area by the door clean?

Does it look welcoming from the outside?

What is it like when you first walk in the office?

Is the décor nice?

Is there a nice smell (fragrance)?

Is the front office person personable and smiling?

Is the front area clean and pretty?

How is your waiting room?

Is there music? It should be relaxing and comforting to the patients. I like rock, rap, and hip hop when I work out. It is not appropriate for the office, however.

Is it clean?

Are there new, diverse and interesting magazines for patients to read?

Is it spacious enough for families and kids?

Are there cool toys for kids to play with? Or coloring books?

Are you dressed well? Is your staff dressed well?

You want to be professional. Not everyone agrees with me here, but wearing scrubs is not your best choice. If you or your staff wears them, they may be perceived as lazy. Take it up a notch and leave an impression by looking super professional.

How is your personal office?

I try to keep it clean and uncluttered. Since I meet all my patients in this office, I don't want them to associate a cluttered office with a doctor who has a cluttered mind.

Do you take time with the patient?

I have a personal office and nice mahogany desk where patients talk to me first and then we move to the exam room. We wrap up at the end in my personal office. Sure I could skip some of this but try not to. Going the extra mile sticks in their minds.

Is the exam room clean and equipped well?

Make sure you change out the paper on the exam table and have it cleaned after every patient. I used to work for a group who rarely cleaned except for a mediocre crew at night. I used to see needle syringe caps on the floor all the time. There were bugs in the light coverings. These little things drove me nuts. It leaves an impression with patients as well.

How is the furniture in the office? Clean?

Please make sure everything is clean. There should be nothing on the floor. No dirt. No paper clips. Make things perfect.

Remember the small things about patients. Where do they work? Any hobbies? What can you casually know and mention, if appropriate, that shows you care?

This is not to be a fake thing. Flattery is not what I am talking about, but if a patient tells you they are going to Walt Disney World and you see them a month later, then ask them about it.

Is there a good plan and a nice goodbye on the way out for the patient?

You always need to have them leaving with a smile. "Have I answered all your questions today?" should be a common ritual for you.

This list will grow as more and more people give me feedback, but the point it is that your patient's experience needs to be effective and memorable. This is how word of mouth marketing works. It is also how you make your practice better than everybody else's.

You can read lots of books on this and I mentioned a few, but here a couple I recommend:

- The Starbucks Experience

- Everything is Marketing

- It All Starts With Marketing

Do not take this chapter lightly. You need to pay attention to the details and deliver a great experience. This is not to say you should neglect your job because you do need to give great care but that is not enough in the DPC game. You need to deliver this experience because you need to show that you are worth the monthly cost.

10. The Meet-and-Greet

I think one of the most important things to offer prospective patients is a chance to sit down with you, the doctor, to discuss how the practice may be a fit for them. This is not a free consultation. This is a slot (we give 15-30 minutes) in your day to explain what you do and answer their questions. Many patients need to speak with you and be in front of you before they trust this concept. They need to know you are for real. They need to have their questions answered. They also want to have a connection with the person to which they are paying a monthly fee. If you can be open, transparent and honest then you can convert them into finally joining. You need to smile. You need to be caring. You need not to fake these two things. I usually convert over 80% of these people into patients.

The meet and greet is also a chance to NOT take some patients. Heresy, you say? Nope. I believe I talk 1 out of 20 patients into not joining. Why? Because they are looking for things I cannot deliver. Some are looking for a detective to find that magical thing wrong with them. They want CSI: Primary Care. I usually ask them about who they have seen before and then I tell them that I cannot promise anything other than being an attentive and caring doctor.

There are patients who you just know you are not going to click with or them with you. It took me a while to get past the lost revenue issue, but in the long run it saves so much heartache. There are some people who you know are going to test you. Some just seem angry and distrustful. Some think they will need to come in weekly forever. There are narcotic seekers who you need to probe more deeply to see if they are just coming to get a $80 monthly fee of free pain meds prescriptions to sell on the streets. I had one patient who I told not to join because I did not feel comfortable giving him pain meds and his story was pretty fishy as well. I recommend he not join and to find another doctor, but he was persistent. I think because he had been through every other doctor around. He joined online, but I did not process the transaction.

Instead, I told him that I would accept him as a patient if he agreed that I would not ever give him a narcotic or benzodiazepam. He wrote me a long email accusing me of profiling. Blah, blah, blah. I told him again that he can join but he needed to agree to my terms. He wrote back another long email without ever agreeing. His girlfriend then wrote me a nasty email. I apologized profusely and never processed his transaction.

Whatever the reason, you need to hold your ground if you think it will be a bad match. Just tell them that you don't think this is a great fit for them. Some will appreciate that. Some won't. Be nice. Smile. Tell them you are doing it for them. Let me tell you another story of someone I turned down at a meet and greet. This gentleman came in with his wife. He was not happy with the local large family practice group and he had a legitimate complaint. His issue was insomnia and had not been seen in a long time. A nurse practitioner saw him and did some labs. She called him to say to that he had high cholesterol and low D. They then told him they would call in some medications, which they never did, and never dealt with his insomnia. His multiple calls to them were never returned. So, he complaints were valid. I empathized with him and assured him that though I cannot guarantee to fix his sleep problems, I would give him the time and attention needed. So far, so good. And all true. Then he asked if I work on Saturdays. I said only for emergencies. He stated that he will join if I opened up the clinic for him on Saturdays because he works out of town. I said I would not do that. I said I have a family and I would not change my schedule for him. He was offended, but I didn't waiver. I may have waivered when I was dying to get patients to join but not now. I recommend you do not give in to these types of requests either. I then asked this gentleman if he has any sick days and he says he has tons. I followed this with a question on whether he can use a day here or there on a Friday or Monday so that I can see him. He said he could, but he didn't want to change his schedule to do so. "But it is okay to inconvenience mine?" I asked. He never got it. He never joined because from that point on I pushed him in the other direction and gave him names of other offices to call.

Remember, this is your practice. You do not have a boss to answer to. You do, however, have patients who are customers and they need to be satisfied. If you see someone at a meet and greet whom you know you will never satisfy then cut your losses before you start. Do the old George Costanza routine, which goes "It's not you, it's me." Remember, you don't need to be rude because an unhappy potential customer may tell a lot of people. You want them to say to his or her friends, "No, I didn't join. He was very nice and honest, but felt that he didn't think he could meet my needs."

Lastly, don't let this question the need for a meet and greet. You want patients and some need to "touch" the product before they buy. It is by far the single most effective marketing tool that I used and suggest that people to use it all the time. I never stopped doing them.

11. What Makes Your Practice Unique?

Every DPC practice has a bunch of commonalities. I have tried to list many of them below. These separate us from the industrialized medicine model. Feel free to use these sound bites for marketing. They may also help you brainstorm to find other ways to make you better than the rest. And we are better.

Old But New

Your model isn't new. A customer paying the store directly is an old concept. Insurance has been in this crappy form for only 40 or so years and it has changed medicine for the worst. Your model is more like the original family medicine model, an homage to the great docs of yesteryear and not the Frankencare you see today. Get this information out there.

Personable

You know your patients because they are people and not numbers.

Accessible

You have less patients and spend more time with the ones you have.

Comprehensive

You can now feel complete in each unhurried visit.

No interference from insurance companies.

You remove the red tape and bureaucracy from seeing patients.

You pay attention to the patient.

You do not sit in the room staring at the computer.

You remove the middleman from the doctor's office.

Random Tips and Ideas:

- Using a membership model, patients get unrestricted access to their doctor and most services for just a monthly fee.

- We can be more proactive and have the time to discuss wellness.

- What you offer more than anything else is time: Time to listen, time to ask questions and explain, time to think about problems, time to return phone calls promptly, time to relay test results personally, and time to be there for your patients and their families when they need it. How? We only have 600 Total Patients (normally, it's about 2,500 for a primary care doctor).

- At Forest Direct Primary Care, we bill the patient directly on a monthly fee basis. It's like a gym membership. That allows us more time with each patient (30-60 min) and it eliminates all CODING! And staring at the computer.

- No Copays, Unlimited Number of Visits.

- Skin Procedures, Exercise and Nutrition Prescriptions, Osteopathic Manipulation and more– ALL INCLUDED!

Better experience

- Talk directly to your doctor by email, text, or phone any time of the day or night.
- The old time family doctor approach, Marcus Welby, MD.

- Less drugs and more chances for natural approaches, diet and exercise to work.

- Patients get concierge care at an affordable price.

Cheaper Labs

Give examples of how patients are getting gouged by getting labs done elsewhere. Your pricing will be cheaper and may even save them their whole membership fee. Use real world examples and numbers. I once had a patient go to a major university medical system for their labs and it cost them $1700. If they had done it at my lab, it would have cost $115. True story, and patients are really shocked and moved by this type of real example.

Anything else?

I do OSTEOPATHIC MANIPULATION TREATMENT or OMT even though I am an MD. It's a hands on way to diagnose and treat back injuries and very similar to chiropractic care. It is free to patients and they love it. Do you have anything else of added value you can offer? Some docs do free yoga sessions for patients and hire an instructor for that. Others have tool like a portable DEXA scan or spirometry. How about using real liquid nitrogen for cryotherapy? Compare that to the cost of going to a dermatologist's office which will charge an office fee and procedure fee.

The biggest question we hear is "why do I need your service when I have insurance?" The answer is that all you really have is an expensive catastrophic plan that pays for almost nothing. As per the article, patients now don't want to go to the doctor. At (blank) Direct Primary Care they come, on average, about six times a year. We get you a 80-90% discount on labs and we help you navigate cheaper meds, cheaper diagnostic testing and cheaper radiological procedures. All this and you get a great office experience. It's concierge care for regular folk.

I have insurance. Why would I still choose (blank) DPC?

You have to have insurance. Most people are getting high deductible plans which is what the insurance companies want. They don't want to pay for anything. So you basically have catastrophic insurance.

Why (blank) DPC is a great fit for businesses:

- Offering a Direct Primary Care service with your current benefits plans provides employees quality care while saving you money. It's time to incorporate Forest DPC in your medical offerings.

- (blank) DPC can take care of 90% of the healthcare services you need. Take advantage of this opportunity to provide quality care for your employees, which can also help you attract and retain new employees.

- Your employees will be delighted with our highly personalized service and unbeatable convenience. Members enjoy great access and care, and plans can lower costs while improving member health. No matter the size of your organization, (blank) DPC is the right choice for your employees and your bottom line.

- Studies show that DPC Delivers 20 Percent Lower Overall Healthcare Costs, Increases Patient Satisfaction. The Qliance study from 2015 showed that the increasingly popular "direct primary care" model, with its emphasis on unrestricted access to primary care, makes healthcare 20 percent less expensive than traditional health insurance yet leaves patients feeling more satisfied with their care.

12. Get Your Scripts Down

You really want consistency in your pitch. That means anything said to patients, prospective patients or curious bystanders should be said the same time and time again by every staff member in your office. A consistent and clear message is the key. How do you do that? Well, first you have to figure what works for you. Which lines grab people emotionally? Which things, when said, get them to finally sign up? What are the clear answers to their common questions that make them truly understand the concept? The truth is that you will hear the same questions over and over. You have read my pitch to patients in a previous chapter. I have that memorized. I also have my staff collect and write down the common questions they hear all the time and clarify their answers. Here are some examples:

Possible Questions from Potential Patients

"Why should I pay a monthly fee for your services if I already have insurance?"

At any other primary care office, you are going to be paying a co-pay and then on top of that, you will have an office visit charge of at least $150.00. That is not including any additional charges for blood work or kit testing (ex. flu, strep, mono, etc.) that they might do during your visit. At our office, blood work is roughly 90% discounted when billed with us and all necessary kit testing is covered under your monthly fee. There are no co-pays or office visit charges and we offer full transparency with all payments. Most insurance policies are high deductible plans and most patients will never reach that amount in a year so you will be paying everything out of pocket at other offices anyway. But, in our office, you are getting more time with Dr. Farrago. All visits are either 30 minutes or an hour instead of 5 to 7 minutes at any other office.

"Can Dr. Farrago make referrals to specialists?"

Yes, he can refer you to specialists. If you have insurance and wish to use that at the specialist's office, be mindful that you might need

61

a prior authorization. If you are unsure about this, just contact your insurance carrier and see what is required. We will be glad to take care of things from that point.

"What if I have to go to the hospital?"

If you are hospitalized, an admitting doctor or hospitalist will care for you during your stay in the hospital. Dr. Farrago does not do hospital work anymore but will follow up with you during and after your hospitalization. We will obtain records from the hospital once you are discharged and add them to your chart.

"Lab work - How does this work and where does it get sent too?"

Blood work is drawn in the office and the majority of the time, requires you to be fasting for 12 hours. Lots of water is highly recommended! We use LabCorp in Burlington, NC for testing and there is a courier that comes by the office daily to pick up the samples. The turnaround time on results is usually 24-48 hours depending on the panels being tested. Patients can bill through us (roughly 90% discounted) or they can file through their insurance company (if insured) but since all plans vary in what is covered and what is not, we cannot guarantee that you will not be paying a lot out of pocket if your plan doesn't cover all of the tests that Dr. Farrago wants check. You can check with your insurance company beforehand and we can let you know our total so that you can make the best decision.

Is there a contract when joining?

We have no contract. We are strictly a month to month membership practice. We don't want you to have to stay if you don't like it here.

"What is OMT?"

OMT or osteopathic manipulation treatment is one of the great services Dr. Farrago provides for his patients. He is the only MD in the area to provide this. OMT involves manipulating areas of the body to alleviate pain and discomfort in the neck, shoulders, back and legs. There is no extra cost for this service.

"If I join now, can I add my spouse and/or family to my enrollment later?"

If we still have room, OF COURSE! This is how it would work. If just one person signs up there is an $80 registration fee and $80 first month billing. If anyone additional is added, there will be another $80 registration fee and the monthly billing will vary to make up the difference (going to couple plan or family plan). If a couple signs up and wants to add children later the billing will be $165 for the registration fee (max) and $135 for couple plan. When the kids are added, there will not be a registration fee and the monthly payment will become $165 for the family. $30 per kid for a max of $165 for the family plan. For growing families, there will not be any additional fees for adding more kids.

"Does Dr. Farrago do dermatological work in office or will he refer out to dermatology?"

Dr. Farrago can handle most dermatological needs in office. He routinely performs skin checks on patients and if he thinks a spot needs attention he will provide it. He performs cryotherapy for wart removal and skin tag removal, which is covered under your monthly payment. If it is something more suspicious, he will biopsy the site and will send it to a pathologist for review. To have a sample biopsied runs $75.00 and that is for the pathology fee to read the sample. We do not bill for anything else. The procedure that Dr. Farrago performs is free. We get the reports back and if the sample was abnormal or requires further work-up, Dr. Farrago will refer you to a local dermatologist. Either way, he will follow up with you regarding your results.

"Does Dr. Farrago do gynecological exams in office or does he refer out?"

Dr. Farrago, with consent from the patient, can perform manual breast exams in office as well as pap smears and bimanual exams. If a patient is not comfortable having either of those done, the patient can choose to be referred to a gynecologist. It is a service we provide to our "of age" female patients. If you choose to have your pap smear done with us, our price is $30 and that is just to have pathology read the sample. We do not bill for anything else. When we get the report back, he will follow up with you to let you know what the report showed. If the sample comes back abnormal, we will refer out to the gynecologist for further work ups.

"For female patients, will someone other than just Dr. Farrago be in the room during exams?"

Christine, his assistant, will be in the room with you and the doctor throughout the exam.

13. How Quickly Will I Fill My Practice?

The most common question and concern I get from docs thinking about going into DPC is "How quickly will I fill my practice?" For which I answer, "Who the f%ck knows?!?" I know that sounds rude, but if you want guarantees than work for the man. The success of DPC depends on tons of variables. What are they? Well, you read them all in this book. If you fail to give great service, fail to have great staff, fail to market yourself and so on then it is going to take you a VERY long time to fill.

Doing all the stuff I mention here (as well as any other resources you use) only guarantees you the best chances of filling and filling more quickly. Chances. That is the key word. There have been a few DPC docs who, for whatever, reason have struggled. Nothing in life is guaranteed, but if you go to Las Vegas and want to gamble then you want the best odds on your sides. And DPC has much higher odds, especially if you follow the advice you were given.

Here is my month-by-month growth from when I started my practice. I sold my practice in October of 2020. I was at about 560 at that time. Why the decrease in the summer of 2019? Well, I helped a fellow doc, as mentioned previously, open his DPC practice across town. I lost a few patients to him who lived near his new office. From that point, there were two docs trying to get new patients. This makes things a little harder because there is always churn or turnover (see my book *Slowing the Churn in Direct Primary Care While Also Keeping Your Sanity*).

Will this growth pattern be the same for you? See my first sentence in this section for the answer. Everyone and every place is different. All I can do is show my stuff, which is pretty much the average from speaking to others. The rest is up to you. Work hard. Grind. And you got this.

Month	Patients
Jul/2014	1
Aug/2014	1
Sep/2014	13
Oct/2014	43
Nov/2014	115
Dec/2014	160
Jan/2015	197
Feb/2015	221
Mar/2015	256
Apr/2015	273
May/2015	294
Jun/2015	295
Jul/2015	318
Aug/2015	339
Sep/2015	357
Oct/2015	372
Nov/2015	387
Dec/2015	412
Jan/2016	434
Feb/2016	458
Mar/2016	485
Apr/2016	503
May/2016	509
Jun/2016	509

Jul/2016	516
Aug/2016	520
Sep/2016	548
Oct/2016	580
Nov/2016	634
Dec/2016	613
Jan/2017	604
Feb/2017	604
Mar/2017	611
Apr/2017	624
May/2017	620
Jun/2017	619
Jul/2017	630
Aug/2017	626
Sep/2017	627
Oct/2017	626
Nov/2017	634
Dec/2017	646
Jan/2018	651
Feb/2018	659
Mar/2018	661
Apr/2018	662
May/2018	650
Jun/2018	644
Jul/2018	634

Aug/2018	640
Sep/2018	647
Oct/2018	632
Nov/2018	625
Dec/2018	625
Jan/2019	624
Feb/2019	620
Mar/2019	609
Apr/2019	608
May/2019	607
Jun/2019	608
Jul/2019	606
Aug/2019	603
Sep/2019	593
Oct/2019	584
Nov/2019	587
Dec/2019	590
Jan/2020	575
Feb/2020	567
Mar/2020	566
Apr/2020	562
May/2020	557
Jun/2020	551

SECTION THREE

Let's Market This Thing!

1. Marketing your practice

This book could actually be all about marketing because that is what you really want, isn't it? You want to drive patients to your practice so that it fills and the bank account increases. I get it. I was there. The problem is that there are no easy answers to marketing your practice. There definitely isn't one perfect way. DPC docs are constantly looking to find new ways to get patients. It is what we all initially perseverate about. You will too. That being said, you need to remember a few things.

Word of mouth is crucial

If you spend all your time trying to get other patients, you may neglect the ones right in front of you. Don't do that! Make that patient feel special so that he wll spread the word about you. Screw that up and it can haunt you for a long time.

Every doctor and every community is different

Some areas respond better to some attempts at marketing. I have known some DPC docs do well on the radio, but only on certain stations. Others do print ads but this is rare. Facebook, addressed later on, can also work.

Trial and error

Sometimes, after you do your research, you just need to try a few things and then go where the nibbles are.

The other thing about marketing that you need to know is that there never will be a lack of experts or salesmen trying to have you pay them. Don't do it. Here are some examples:

Consultants

Some are DPC docs and some are just, well, business people. They promise you the world. All I can say is buyer beware.

Marketers

These are people in your community who somehow believe they know how to get you customers. Don't believe them. Most don't even know what DPC is.

Salespeople

Beware of the dude who walks in trying to "learn about the practice" who then turns out to be a salesman who is trying to sell you his product. It will happen at least a half dozen times for you, trust me. It is disingenuous and wrong, but you have to try and play nice. If they insinuate that if buy some radio spots, they will join your practice, do not believe them! This happened to me four times in the first few months of opening and they lied every time.

Once you have your place open for business, then you want to start getting patients. But won't they just show up? No. Word of mouth will work, but that may take 6 to 12 months. That sucks. You want patients and you want them now! Sorry, life doesn't work that way. This may be counterintuitive but I think growing your practice too quickly is actually problematic. In fact, getting all 600 patients at once may sound great, but you won't be able to start getting them in to be seen like you promised. You will lose your credibility and will become overwhelmed. There is a delicate balance between getting people to join up quickly enough to keep ahead of expenses versus getting too much interest and failing in that respect. The latter is rare, however. In my opinion, getting about 20-30 to join per month is the right number.

Slow and steady is the key. So what works? I think that is the mystery answer and no one knows the right one. In my opinion, you need to constantly be reading marketing books and articles. You need to trial and error different options. And you need to keep costs low. The following chapters are examples that have worked for me and others, but before I can share them with you I must make sure you do one thing: deliver a great DPC experience.

2. The Experts

While DPC is growing, it is still relatively small. Right now the pioneers are being propped up as experts and that may or may not be true. I will mention one. Josh Umbehr and I have known each other for years. It started when he was about a year out into his DPC practice and I contacted him. He has always been forthcoming on his advice and his experiences. We kept in touch and then years later when I opened my practice he was the one I used as a mentor. I mentioned before that I also use his software. Josh is a great speaker and has been at the forefront of the DPC movement. He is not a consultant and does not charge as one. Of course, that may change, but I can attest to his expertise.

There have been other doctors out there and you probably have heard of them. I am not going to mention names and I do not know how great they are. Many of them charge a lot of money even to talk to on the phone. I get it. They are capitalizing on this movement and they get "used" a lot by random cold calls asking for help. So I understand why they charge what they do. I am just not sure their prices are worth it. I also don't like commitments (I have heard some for up to 5 years) of an annual fee. Honestly, if you don't understand DPC after doing it for a year, then this may not be for you.

I am now an expert. Why? For no other reason than the fact that I have done it and wrote this book. It has taken time, research and experience to get here. Am I the best? I have no idea. I do like lecturing and have gotten better at understanding all questions by answering them at my talks. I have a wide reach of my network through my 13 year-old blog (authenticmedicine.com) as well as my FB group. That being said, I make no promises that I can make you a great DPC doc or make your practice successful. A lot of that falls on you. So, no other expert should promise you that either.

What about no-doctors as experts? I am sure they know a lot of information, but please don't believe they are the same as a doctor who has plunged into a DPC career. No way. No how.

If you have plenty of money to burn, then go ahead and hire a consultant. If not, then reconsider. Be careful. Again, buyer beware. You can get a lot, if not more information, by reading this book, going to conferences, visiting other DPC offices, and talking with me or others via email, phone, or via FB.

3. Word of Mouth

I am asked all the time "How do you get patients?" What you are going to hear most from other DPC doctors is that word of mouth is critical. This is true, but you will blow it off. Why? The reason is that you need enough patients talking about you to get that word of mouth. It is a tipping point phenomenon, which doesn't really help you when you are just starting out. So, you have to get the ball rolling with other techniques as described in this book before the word of mouth program can take hold. So, use Facebook, get an article in the paper, do local lectures, join a BNI or "leads" groups, join other business groups, and then hopefully you will get word of mouth.

So, why did I say hopefully? Because you truly need to make your office special. You need to give great service to your patients so that they have something to brag about. They need to brag with statements like:

I love my doctor.

I trust my doctor.

My doctor says....

I love the staff at my doctor's office.

I love going to see the doctor.

My doctor helped me to....

I never wait at my doctor's office.

I always get the time I need with my doctor.

My doctor is so nice and personable.

My doctor is always available to ask a question.

Doing this is not that easy, by the way. Sure, at first you will have time and your motivation will be high. As time goes by, you may slip and fall into old habits. Don't. Your reputation is always on the line. Not only can word of mouth fill your practice, but it can also decimate you if you get negative word of mouth. The choice is yours.

4. Tips on Getting the Word Out (Creating Buzz)

The first thing you need to do is contact the local media. This includes the local papers, the local radio, the local TV stations and any other social media can find. You absolutely HAVE to get an article or articles done on your practice. Spoon-feed reporters if you have to. What do you sell? You want to read other articles about DPC docs (just do a Google search or go to DPCNews) so you can see the common thing themes and sound bites these reporters want, write or talk about. They love the personal approach. They love the way you are eschewing the system. They love that you hate the insurance companies. They love that you will do house calls, that is if you do. They love the old school approach of medicine. Do your research. Send them emails. Call them. Write them. Do NOT, however, tell other media that you are talking to anyone else or they will kill the story. Get as many done at one time as you can. I had an article in the local paper, and this got picked up by another town's newspaper. Great. At the same time the local TV station came over. Then the local business magazines talked to me. I never mentioned that they were all talking to me. I wanted as much press at the same time to start a tipping point for patients. It worked. Remember, you get one shot at this so don't screw it up. The media will not come back to you in three, six or nine months to see how you are doing. This is it. Per Eminem, "Look, if you had, one shot, or one opportunity to seize everything you ever wanted. In one moment would you capture it, or just let it slip?" Just don't throw up mom's spaghetti.

Open house

You may need to advertise this and it is worth it. You may want to schedule this before the article mentioned above comes out so that the writer may put the meeting information in the article and then hopefully more people will show up. That is free advertising. These are not as rewarding as you would think but you will get the word out and educate as many people as you can. They are draining. I only did one, but you many want to do it multiple times. A pure open house is different. The open forum should start with a PowerPoint or a fifteen-minute talk by you and then let the questions fly. An open house is where you sit around with your staff for a few hours, and anyone can come in and poke around your place. This leads to questions and may lead to new patients. I hate them, but they are worth it.

Radio

This has worked for some people. You will be inundated with salespeople, many who will disguise themselves as prospective patients, trying to get you to buy ads. It didn't impress me and many of my DPC buddies have said the same. That does not mean it won't work and I do know of someone who got a lot of patients after his ad. Buyer beware, though. We did do a very local radio station ad for three months that got us a few patients but that is all.

Print Ads

These are expensive and usually don't work. I have tried the local evergreen magazines that sit around at the grocery store all year, and the results were mediocre. The price for a newspaper ad was not even close for me to try. I had a "pay for play" ad where I paid a few hundred bucks to have a local business magazine use me as an expert and get a nice pic and quote. I felt dirty after I did it and would never do it again. Learn from me. Never pay to have an article written about you. Ever.

Videos

I bartered (see a later section) to have three one-minute videos that I had made. I used them on my website and on FB. It works well for people who want to actually see and hear the doctor they are going to pay for. These videos can be used for TV or as sound bites for radio ads.

TV

I think this is an expensive game and better when you have money to blow, but who has that? The price is high and this concept of DPC, may not be ready for prime time or even late night watchers.

Quirky ads

I have not used Valu Paks, but I have heard positive stuff about them. I have seen a local realtor use the movie theater commercials, billboards, shopping carts, and every "sponsorship" you can imagine. Do they work? I assume they do for her. I watch what new methods she uses, and then consider them for myself.

Billboards

They're a possibility, but make sure it is cost-friendly and make sure your ad is not too small so it can be seen by cars passing by.

Grocery carts

Many big chain grocery stores offer opportunities to put your ad right on their carts. This can be costly but would get your name out there.

Targeted mailings

This is available through the post office and even some online services. You probably want to make a postcard or some other advertisement that works with their requirements. You would also want to target areas of people who you know would be interested and could afford your services.

Local schools

You can advertise at local school theatre productions in their playbill or sponsor a local sports team.

Connect with local moms' groups and newcomers' groups

Advertise in neighborhood newsletters

Connect with homeschooling groups

Do lectures for the public (discussed in another chapter)

5. Using Facebook

Using Facebook can be very interesting and can be a great marketing tool. In fact, it is my favorite. Why? Because it is relatively cheap and you can truly hit your market. Many of the kids have left FB but the young moms and middle-age women are still on it. And they are the medical decision makers.

So where do you start? You first need to create your DPC practice page. Get all the information on there including pictures, maps, website address, office hours, phone number, etc. Then you need to promote your page to your local community, which is important to start getting people who are potential patients to join.

The first thing I would recommend is getting your current patients, as few as they may be, to like your practice on Facebook. That enables every future post of yours to be posted on their Facebook page. This gets the ball rolling. Now you want to start posting information. That information is obviously up to you. What I tend to talk about is the broken healthcare system and I use articles as links to describe what I'm talking about. I figure the enemy of my enemy is my friend. Then, I compare about how Direct Primary Care truly breaks that system and how my office is a Direct Primary Care office. I usually end every post normally stating that they can call my office number to set up a meet and greet with Dr. Farrago. This gets many people in the community to start liking the post and possibly my practice page. It also may get them to wander on that page and think about looking more seriously into what I offer. That is what you want. I usually leave my website address as well so patients can join directly on there.

You can boost your page to get more people to like you in the community or you can boost your post and that gets more people to like you in the community as well. You want to tweak who you want to read these posts. This means setting up the demographics of these posts to be the area your practice is and the age of the people you want to send to. This is just easy advertising, but remember, it may take seven times of interaction before someone finally decides to join your practice. These posts can get somewhat expensive so be careful on how you do this. Also, be very careful on what kind of material you put on there so it is not too offensive or too controversial.

My most popular posts:

Picture of a doctor staring at a computer instead of the patient.

If you are okay with your doctor bringing the computer in the exam room, never looking at you, and typing away as you talk (and not really listening), then PLEASE stay at the medical practice where you are at now. (Blank) Direct Primary Care is not for you. The 30-60 minutes to go through all your problems, the doctor listening and making eye contact, and the feeling of satisfaction that your healthcare needs were met are what we pride ourselves on. If you are fed up, however, with what you see in the picture, then give us a call xxx-2455. We do not bill insurance and we are not insurance. We provide a monthly membership model where you pay $80 a month and you can see us as often as you need. See more at www.xxdpc.com.

Picture of an EMPTY PARKING LOT and EMPTY WAITING ROOM

I commonly have to explain to people who come for a meet and greet that no, we are not going out of business. Our parking lot is usually empty as well as our waiting room, which we call a family room. The reason is that my appointments are 30 to 60 minutes long, and I only am taking a total of 600 patients. Most docs have over 3000 patients. Because of this, you have no problem finding a place to park, and no one is coughing on you in the waiting room. On the rare chance you are waiting (this happens less then a half dozen times in a year), then you can sit back with some coffee or water and listen to some music, read or check your phone. The environment and style of this practice is clean, relaxing and personal. Please check out www.xxdpc.com as we are taking only about 100 more patients.

UPDATE: Facebook got greedy. They will not share all your posts to all the people who like your page. They want you to buy ads. This sucks. It is still the best way to go, however, as the ads in your small market are not that expensive.

6. Getting Other Doctors and Their Families to Be Your Patients

One thing you have to remember is that you are the best family doctor in town. How do I know that? Well, I don't. What I do know is that if I had to put my money on someone getting things right, then I would place it on the doctor who has more time. That would be you.

Now who would truly appreciate your time and reputation? That would be other doctors. I would try to get to the specialists first. One reason is that every family doctor who is in the industrialized model may hate you because they have Death Row Syndrome. Also, family doctors tend to treat themselves and their families. They are also broke, bitter and miserable and would rather eat their firstborn than pay you a monthly fee.

That leaves the specialists. They want the best care for themselves and their families. They also have money. Remember that green stuff that we didn't get by going into this specialty? Yup, it is going to them, and they have a lot of it. They can easily afford your care and would appreciate the time you can offer. They will have peace of mind knowing that their wife or husband and kids have the best care. That goes well with the mansion and the yacht. Sorry, did I just write that?

Lastly, doctors don't like their info in the hospital- wide computer system. We all know how safe that really is from prying eyes? No cardiologist wants his depression listed for a tech to see. This is much more important than you may realize. Guess what? I would bet your EMR is NOT used by anyone else in the local medical community, which means to them, it is safe!

So how do you get to the doctors? Well, if you know them or their emails, then pitch it that way. If you don't, then I recommend you call up the chief of the service and just ask to go to one of their monthly meetings. Tell them you only want 5 minutes to introduce what your practice is due to all the confusion. And I would keep to that. Then after you ask for any more questions tell them, "You know, my practice is perfect for docs and their families. Other doctors I have as patients love the attention for their families, and they even love having their personal medical information out of the shared computer system." Then drop off brochures and go. A week later, send each one a personal letter with a brochure in it. Then sit back and let them come calling. Or not. But at least you gave it a shot, and they have you in mind for the future or for patients who ask for their opinions on a great doctor. And as this section started, one thing you have to remember is that you are the best family doctor in town.

7. Network, Network, Network

You need to get your name out there. You need to get your concept out there. For some reason this is foreign to people. They cannot conceive that they don't need insurance for doctor visits. They cannot conceive that there is a better way to see patients with lots of time in a friendly, clean and relaxed environment. You need to teach them and then they will teach others. Who are they? Anyone! You see those crazy people proselytizing about some bogus supplements in a multi-level marketing and pyramid scheme? Well, they are selling snake oil. You are selling the best care in the land. Actually, you are not even selling. You are educating people about a better way

You need to join local groups that will help you get the word out.

Here are some examples:

- Chamber of Commerce and "leads" groups through the

Chamber of Commerce

- Other business groups like BNI (Business Network International)

- Churches

- Newcomers' Groups

- Local Neighborhood Associations

- Schools

- Sports' Organizations

- Moms' Groups

The following are some other miscellaneous ideas:

Independent insurance agents

These people set up people for insurance and are always asked about good local doctors.

Pharmacists

A local independent pharmacy opened up and he came to me guaranteeing cheaper prices for cash. I put his flyers on in my office and vice versa. Pharmacists get asked all the time about good doctors in the community.

Physical Therapists

I work with one who is doing an all cash-pay practice. She eventually started an alternative group of medical personnel who don't take insurance and we meet regularly to share ideas.

Local Wellness Groups
Gyms

Acupuncturists

Yoga studios

Executives

You need to meet with people one-on-one. Bring some coffee or lunch. Yes, you have now become the drug rep, but your livelihood depends on this. Who do you meet with? How about local business owners? I meet with two guys who have their own businesses. We do breakfast monthly. I pick their brains. I keep them updated, and they send me patients.

8. Making Your Website Work for You

This may sound crazy, but your website is still your most important place to educate potential patients. It should have ALL the information about you, your office, your staff, what services you offer, what DPC is, and on and on. With a new product, like DPC, you need a storage house for this information. This is the first thing people look at when they are interested.

Do you need someone to build it for you? I don't think so. I have built so many websites using Wordpress that I am not sure anyone needs that much help. There are tons of templates that are free so I can't see paying a bunch of money for a third party to use the same method. This does not make you a bad person if you do need this help, but understand that you could be billed thousands for something that isn't that hard to do yourself. This being said, the most important thing to do is get your information down. Go ahead and write everything out and then search the websites of other DPC docs and see what they wrote. Tweak the good stuff. Ask permission if you have to. You are NOT reinventing the wheel here. There are literally thousands of good DPC websites.

So, there you have it. Build a place that stores all your information. Work with Atlas MD (or other EMR company) to integrate their sign-up form into your website. Now, if people want to search for you then they can see everything about you and your office. But what if you don't come up on a search?

Search engine optimization (SEO) is a moving target, and there is an industry of people trying to capitalize on this. You get hit with a million spam attempts that promise to get you on top of the search page for your practice. In other words, it would be great if someone searched family doctor in your town, and your office came up first. It isn't that easy. The goal would be to get Google to show your practice when someone searches Direct Primary Care. You can do some things on your website that may help this. If you are working with a tech person, then ask her to use plug-ins that optimize SEO.   One example may be Yoast SEO. If you are doing it yourself then you have to add that plug-in and follow the directions on how to seed your pages with the right keywords, etc. This is WAAAAY beyond the scope of this book, but it isn't massively hard. Heck, when you are starting out all, you will have is time.

The next piece is to integrate Google analytics into your website so you can see how you are doing. They will send you a monthly performance page to see how many clicks and impressions occur from your website. You can see which pages are being clicked on, and how people find you. You can even see what search terms are being used. Take this information and adjust your website to work for you.

Listen, there are some simple things you can do to optimize your site so people can find you. Don't pay for Google Ads. Don't pay for someone to optimize your SEO. Learn this stuff on your own. The bigger issue is what are you going to do once someone lands on your page?

9. The Sales Funnel

You hear a ton of information about "sales funnels" that are very confusing. It shouldn't be. Think of it as leaving small pieces of cheese so that a potential patient gets closer and closer to signing up.

First, it could be word-of-mouth. Then it is your website where they learn about you. It may be an article on the web. They may call your office. You may see them for a meet-and-greet, and then you finally get them to join.

All this is funneling down the interested patients so that you sign up a fully educated customer. And that is the key word – EDUCATED. The goal of the website, your staff on the phone, your meet-and-greet, etc. is to educate. This is done without pressuring for a sale.

Let me mention some things on my website that really helped this. One was giving them the ability to sign up on a form to have us call them. Now, our number was right there for them to call us to schedule a meet-and-greet. Our email was there too. But we gave them an option to put their name, email and phone number for us to call them. And we promised to do it in 24 hours. People would use this option a lot. I don't know why, but it gave us a chance to prove our service. I captured these names through an email service (Constant Contract) that integrated through my website. We then used these addresses for a couple of follow emails. All to educate. Not as spam.

I think calling a patient within 24 hours was a way for us to show our service. Maybe potential patients were just testing us? Not sure, but we proved ourselves and it enabled us to educate these patients by phone.

The other thing I created was a *Consumer Guide to Primary Care*. This is a large PDF that was free (see Appendix). I put a pop-up menu when you hit my website asking if you wanted it. I also put a form on the site. I also sent it to anyone who gave us their name to call them. Why? Education. The "Guide" is a known commodity in the marketing world. Joe Polish, known for his marketing skills, allows others to copy his guide and so do I. It explains all the problems that the industrialized medical world has, and then shows how DPC fixes most of it. You may copy it and tweak it for your practice.

There you have it. Almost. The last thing I did was make some professionally done videos explaining my practice. These were each one minute long. It talked about DPC in general, about why you would still sign up even if you have insurance, etc. These were embedded on my website. Education! When people signed up for the "Guide" or a request to have us call them, they would receive one email from me with a link for that guide. A week later I would then send them another email seeing if they have any questions and then links to all my videos. Education!

All potential patients received two emails and then I stopped. I was not in the businesses of being a pest. I also didn't keep these email addresses but you can if you want to send another email in a year or so. Just make sure you clean this out of names of people who already joined.

10. Using the Rating Systems

Doctors are being graded all over the place now. It is like we are on parade. The worst part is that these evaluations are anonymous and any idiot who hates you can hurt you by putting in terrible comments about you. I wish there was a great way to rate doctors because I, too, would want to know so I can send my family to the right doctor. It just isn't that easy, and these rating sites are used by many people. Fair or unfair, it doesn't matter. I am well aware that since there are no proven metrics to truly judge physicians, it therefore makes these grades invalid and useless. But you know what? Patients don't care!

Websites like RateMDs or Healthgrades are putting big money into their businesses because patients use their information. So, you can fight them all you want or you can use your close relationships with your patients to your advantage. How? It's easy. Get ranked high. Your supposed competitors, the employed doctors, don't care about these sites. They won't work them to their advantage. You need to. Here is what I did. I sent an email out with the link to these or other rating sites and gently asked my patients to give me some good feedback if they believe I deserve it. They cannot do it from your office because only one feedback/comment can be given per location or IP address. Also, if too many ratings or comments are given on the same day, they will disqualify them all. RateMDs did that with me and there was nothing you I could do about it. Similarly, if one horrible comment is left about you, then good luck in getting rid of it. These companies do not care about you.

So, with all this in mind, is it still worth updating your "grades" on these sites? Yes. You want to use it as a tool to recruit patients. I put "#1 Rated Doctor in Forest, VA by RateMDs" right on my website. I link right to their site. I use this to my advantage and feel good about it. All the comments are by real patients and are how they actually feel. It wipes out any negative ones I had (I had one from years ago in my old employed position in another state) by dilution.

In summary, I don't really believe in the validity of these rating sites, but I am committed to building my DPC practice. If using these things to my advantage helps me, then so be it.

11. Newsletter, Lectures and Email Updates

I want to be connecting to patients as often as I can. I want to remind them that I am still their doctor and that I am giving them value. Why do I do this? I try to look at the worst-case scenario. Remember, they see a bill come their way every month for $80 to $165. When they came in that month, it felt nice that they had that physical or mole removal or joint injection and it only cost that little. When they didn't come in that month, it leaves a little pit in their stomach. They wonder whether they are getting their money's worth. Every month they don't hear from you, touch base with you, or see you is another step toward leaving the practice. This is not true for the majority, but I figure if I can please these people, then I can please the rest. So, there are things I do and you can do too.

Newsletter

Every month I send out an e-newsletter of sorts. I use Constant Contact as my email service. My "update" is not entirely in the email but the email covers some new things going on in the office, info on how to get in touch with me and some type of other tidbits on immunizations, etc. They are then invited to go to my website with a patient-only password where they can see a section of health updates right from me. I may discuss the controversies of cholesterol or the benefits of the Paleo Diet or why blue light is bad at night for them. Not your mainstream stuff, but stuff I am concerned about. They can always leave comments or email me questions or come in and talk to me about it. This personal access combined with the exclusivity of the updates (just for patients) is a value to them.

Lectures

I like public speaking. Others don't and I get that. I also pick topics that not only interest me but interest patients as well. That being said, giving a free lecture to patients and one guest is a nice "exclusivity" piece for them. To be honest, I don't always do that and many times I invite the public to come as well. It is great advertising for the office. You can do it at a local library or maybe health food store. My office is just too small, and after my first cholesterol talk I knew we had to move it. We actually use a local recreation center, and I pay $50 because I have put up to a 100 people in there for one talk. I do these every other month, and I recommend you consider it. I have a portable little projector that was cheap and shoot my power point onto the wall. It works great. Patients love this. If possible, it is a great idea to film these talks as well.

Email Updates

I mentioned that each e-newsletter is started with an email directing them to the updated health section of my website. In these emails I send some community information as well. I also email stuff that is going on acutely. For example, if I see a bad virus going around I tell all my patients via an email and they love it. It is also a way to stop patients from coming in for these things that I really can't help anyway and they appreciate that too. Other info that I may shoot out is some CDC stuff that is applicable locally.

There are more ways to make sure patients feel that your service is valuable. Just jump in and see what works for you. Don't wait! Use trial and error. Trying something is better than trying nothing.

12. College Program

Do you want an easy way to get cash in your practice? My wife thought of this and it is brilliant. I highly recommend you hook up with local colleges to offer "some" of their students a college program deal. What is that, you say? It is whatever you want it to be but we offer local college students to see them for $300 per semester or $550 for the year. They can come as often as they like. They can also email and text, and this age group loves that! The summer and winter vacation periods are not included though, we have some flexibility.

So, why do this? Well, for one, college students tend to have simpler problems, which are easy to handle. The pitch, for parents, is that their kids have their own local concierge doctor who knows the patient well. We are not a campus health clinic. That place, usually a graveyard for retiring or burned out doctors now being staffed mostly by PAs and NPs, is fine for the colds and sprains, etc. What you should be offering is different. You are offering concierge care at a reasonable price for the students who need it. So, for those patients who have complex issues (asthma, depression, diabetes), then many parents want their kids to have some continuity of care by the same medical doctor in town. That is where you come in. But there is another reason for parents to want their kids to come to you. If you have the student sign a release, then the parent can talk to you directly about Jenny's ADD or depression, about Billy's asthma and so on. This is peace of mind.

There is competition for these students, however. There are three colleges where I am located. All three have the big local family practice involved in some manner. Two of them agreed, initially, to hand my brochures out at the freshmen orientation sessions. It didn't happen, however, and we think that the local family practice group put the kibosh on this. All I really wanted, at a maximum, is 200 students but competition is competition so be aware of who yours is. The other university allowed us to contact parents via a controlled email. They also put our college program brochures into their freshman orientation packets as well. By year two, however, only the packets were allowed but not the email. Once again, the local family practice group stepped in. Welcome to the free market.

I spent the extra money making a special college program brochure so the kids have something to read, understand and give to their parents. I explain to them that any out- of -state kids are getting billed in full at the campus or local clinics because they are out of network. With us, they get a fixed cost and peace of mind. It is a good pitch.

I highly recommend you try to do this with your local colleges. It may take some time to get to the right people, but it is worth it. Even 50 students is good money and worth your time.

This, by the way, was our email to college student parents:

Dear Parents (and Students)

We would like to inform you of another health care option that is available this upcoming academic year. If you would like peace of mind knowing that your student has his/her own family doctor right in town, then Forest Direct Primary Care may be a great option. Forest Direct Primary Care, located about 15 minutes from campus, is a concierge medical practice offering personalized care and accessibility for a flat fee of $300 per semester or $550 if you sign up for both semesters. This is not an insurance plan. In fact, Forest Direct Primary Care does not bill any insurance. Instead, this fee covers all office visits, physicals, minor laceration repairs, EKGs, trigger point injections, nebulizer treatments, blood draws and osteopathic manipulation in addition to other services (see complete listing of covered services on website).

This program may be a particularly good fit if:

- Your student has special health care needs.

- You have a high deductible plan.

- You have an out-of-state HMO.

- You are a member of a health sharing ministry.

- You want assurance that your student will have care when he/she needs it.

Dr. Doug Farrago will be your student's physician. Dr. Farrago has twenty years experience in family medicine, sports medicine, urgent care, nutrition and osteopathic manipulation. He is also the inventor of the Knee Saver and the Cryohelmet.

You may learn more about the college program at Forest Direct Primary Care by going to www.forestdirectprimary.com and clicking on the college link.

You may sign up online or you can call the office at 434-616-2455 to sign up.

You may also stop by the office at 1149 Vista Park Drive, Suite C. Forest, VA (off Forest Rd. in the Forest Professional Park).

The Forest Direct Primary Care College Program only has availability to the first 200 students who sign up. So, act promptly if you are interested.

We look forward to being your student's physician this upcoming academic year.

Update: I had a great college program when I started. It fizzled. Why? The local college stole my program and started their own. Ugh. They worked with the large family practice group in town to do this. Such is life. It did bring money in when I started so it was a great boost. It may not be this way for you, but you never know until you try.

13. What is My Pitch?

When I have a potential patient I will say anything to get them to join. I lie. I promise the world. I.. I...I ....am kidding. The truth is that we have to sell ourselves to potential patients all the time, but it is easy if you believe in what you are doing and if you believe in yourself. So, here is how my normal meet and greet pitch goes:

Welcome to my practice.

Smile.

Make eye contact.

How did you find out about us? This is critical to tracking how you get patients.

Great. So what questions do you have for me? Then just listen. Let them talk it out. Answer each question for them to put them at ease.

What is frustrating you about where you are at right now? (This is critical for them to basically sell themselves on a better way. Let them go off on how bad the medical system is because it is.)

I explain how I think we are different:

- More time with patients

- More Accessibile

- More comprehensive

I then go on to say:

So you know how this membership model works, right? (I want to make sure they know what they are getting into. I explain that whether they come in 7 times or none, they will be billed $80. I explain the registration fee with is $80. I make sure they understand).

Do you have any more questions?

I close but do not make them sign anything there. It is not a car dealership. They do need to leave with the feeling FOMA (fear of missing out). I'll mention some things before they leave like:

- I am only taking 600 patients and once I fill up I won't be taking anymore.

- I once had a crappy riding mower and had to get a John Deere a year later. Wish I had got the more expensive one first. You truly get what you pay for.

- If you value your health, which everyone should, then you need to see your doctor when you need or want to. With a high deductible, you will hold off on your care. By paying monthly, you will want to use our service because you are paying for it, which is what we want and it is good care. So, for example, most men, who state they never come to the doctor, come in on average of six times a year.

Many people call the above "elevator pitches" because it challenges you to hone your pitch to 30 seconds or less as if you had to convince someone during an elevator ride. What I listed were things I would say to patients at a meet-and-greet. But what about other times? What if you met a friend of your spouse who was in need of a primary care doctor? Or what about if you met a local businessperson? Or a news reporter? You want to have a few elevator pitches in your toolbox to pull out at any time. Here is an example:

What do you do?

I am a family doc that does direct primary care.

What's direct primary care?

It's a monthly membership model where I work for the patient and not the insurance companies. It allows me to be the doctor my patients' want me to be where I can give them 30-60 minute visits, get them in when they need to get in and give them the time and care they need.....versus the industrialized model where patients are run through like cattle.

Here are some more examples:

- You know how people can't get in to see their doctors and, if they do, it is for about 5 min or less? What DPC does is offer a monthly membership model that allows me to treat a much smaller panel of patients. In fact, since we don't deal with insurance companies we can see patients when they need to be seen, give them 30-60 during each visit and ultimately even save them money.

- At __DPC, we believe that going to the doctor should be simple and affordable. So, we do things differently at our office. Instead of billing health insurance, our patients pay a monthly fee and we see them as often as they need for whatever may ail them. In addition to unlimited appointments, our members have access to discounted labs, like a cholesterol panel for $6, and wholesale meds, like BP meds for $1 and a Zpak for $2. Our patients can call, text or email their doctor directly for any of their concerns. Would you like to learn more or sign up with us?

- We return medicine to a healing relationship between a doctor and a patient rather than a business transaction.

- "What if you didn't have to wait for months to see your physicians, hours in a waiting room to only see your physician for 5 minutes, who doesn't pay attention to you, but instead you can see your physician the same day, not wait, and have him/her spend time with you to answer your concerns? Well you can, with me, at _____!"

Now it is your turn. Work on this. Tweak it. Make it your own. Memorize them, and use them regularly. You have to practice or you will flub it. Try it on people over and over again and you will get great at it. And you will thank me some day .

14. The Healthcare Sharing Ministries

We have a lot of patients who use the Healthcare Sharing Ministries. I highly recommend you check them out, and work with them. These organizations allow patients to be excluded from any penalties for not having insurance. Below is an explanation that I found online:

A health care sharing ministry (HCSM) provides a health care cost sharing arrangement among persons of similar and sincerely held beliefs. HCSMs are operated by not-for-profit religious organizations acting as a clearinghouse for those who have medical expenses and those who desire to share the burden of those medical expenses.

HCSMs receive no funding or grants from government sources.

HCSMs are not insurance companies. HCSM do not assume any risk or guarantee the payment of any medical bill. Twenty-nine states have explicitly recognized this and specifically exempt HCSMs from their insurance codes.

HCSMs serve more than 530,000 people, with participating households in all fifty states.

HCSMs' participants share more than $500 million per year for one another's health care costs.

HCSMs strive to be accessible to participants regardless of their income, because traditionally shares are a fraction of the cost of insurance rates.

Working with HCSM doesn't imply anything other than that you have very transparent and affordable prices for their members. Interestingly enough, though they do not guarantee any payment of medical bills, this system seems to work for many people. Basically, this works like a catastrophic insurance plan and is much cheaper for people. It may end up being a great model for the future. Included in the Appendix is a letter I used for the HCSMs to email their members. It's free advertising and worked really well.

Update: There are other health sharing companies now, like Sedera. The problem is cracking their system and getting them to put your name out there. This is tougher than it should be because they seem to be clueless. I think they like DPC, but are afraid of or ignorant on how we can work together. I still think you need to try and work with them. Some even give discounts to patients who use DPC doctors.

15. Working with Small Businesses

This is an interesting one. Many of you would want to work with a large business that would fill you immediately. I can tell you that this is NOT the way to go. You become dependent on them and if they leave then you are screwed. There is also much more red tape with large businesses. I highly recommend you read this book by Dr. Shane Purcell, a friend and fellow DPC doctor: *Magic, Pixie Dust, and Miracles: A Guide for Direct Primary Care and Employers.*

I cannot summarize his book here, but I will give you my opinion. Get yourself up and running and make sure your practice is humming without snags before you approach businesses. I will include a sample letter in the Appendix that I send to owners of small businesses.

I like the small companies of 20 or less employees, and I like to approach many of them. This is like diversification in your stock portfolio. If one goes sour, you are not sunk. I also like to keep this total number under 100 employees from these multiple businesses. You do not want to be a their occupational health doctor. This brings us to the next point, which is setting boundaries and rules with these companies. In fact, I will list the ones we had:

What Employers Need to Know When Having Their Employees Enrolled at Forest Direct Primary Care:

1. Forest Direct Primary Care is enhanced and personalized healthcare without the interference of insurance companies.

2. We are a family practice, which handles 90% of all medical problems.

3. Your employees will get consistant care with our only doctor, Douglas Farrago M.D.

4. There are no copays or office visit fees.

5. Care is provided in a comfortable environment, without crowds and there is NEVER a wait.

6. We are not an urgent care, though we can deal with all the same issues, even stitches, during our normal business hours.

7. Dr. Farrago is accessible 24/7 via phone, text or email.

8. We offer to be your employee's family doctor if he/she chooses so. They can't have two family doctors. If they want to use us as an "acute care doctor" and keep their own family doctor, then that would be fine and we will deal with only their acute issues during our normal business hours.

9. We usually get people in the same day they contact us, if needed. We have ample openings for this. We prefer not to have people just walk in as not to encroach on someone else's appointment.

10. Limitations:

    a. Most labs are discounted by 90% but are not included.

    b. Pathology is not included but is at steep discount.

    c. We take patients of all ages and with all types of medical problems. We do, however, retain the option of not taking patients we feel are out of the scope of our practice (ex. chronic pain patients, etc). This is decided on a case by case basis.

11. You company will be billed monthly for all your employees that enroll.

    a. $80 a month ($65 a month for ten or more).

    b. There is an $80 a month per person registration fee ($60 per person for ten or more).

    c. All employees must also put their own credit cards on file for other purchases such as labs, etc.

12. For those that choose us as their primary care doctor, then a full physical will be set up. These are about a month out

after signing up and this all depends on how many members sign up.

13. Family memberswho want to join would have to use their own credit card to join and the prices are listed on our website (a spouse would be $80 and the kids are $30 each, per month).

14. We are proud that Forest DPC can be affordable, comprehensive, accessible and personal for all our patients.

The above is something we sent to the company and gave to the employees that signed up. I also recommend possibly going to a company meeting to explain things in person. This prevents so many misunderstandings that may occur later on.

My experience with companies is that your experience will not exactly be mine. We had a welding shop, and few of them joined even though it was free. The ones that did join really had no idea how to utilize us even after seeing them many times. We had a preschool join and they did great. So who knows?

The bottom line is that businesses are a small part of a great DPC practice. They are not essential, but they can really blend well with your other patient base. So how do you get them? Well, I mention sending letters above. This is kind of a cold call but can work. Our leads group through the local Chamber of Commerce worked great as almost half of owners in the group, and many of their employees, joined our practice. Our local leads group met every two weeks. The purpose was to learn about and help promote each other's businesses. Our local leads group was a great way to stay connected to local business leaders who could help spread our information about our practice in the community. Our leads group also gave us a boost of inspiration and camaraderie every time we met. The other possibility is just working the patients you have. As you get patients on board, and you realize many of them are small owners, you slowly pitch what you can do for them and this works out really well.

Update: Creating bonds with other business can be a critical part of building your practice. I do think that joining your local

Chamber of Commerce and local leads groups can be extremely helpful in promoting your business. Plus, it helps with the isolation you may feel when having a solo practice. You will connect with a lot of great people with great business ideas that you may then use in your own practice. It is definitely worth the time. In fact, in 20019 we even won the "Small Business of the Year Award" presented by our local Chamber of Commerce.

SECTION FOUR

Now That You Have a DPC
Practice

1. A Reminder of Why You Are Going the DPC Route

Okay, we have talked about a lot of stuff. This may be scaring you off a little bit. Remember, though, that the biggest reason you are going the DPC route is because most doctors are now burned out and you don't want to be like one of them. My former medical partners and I used to laugh and mock burned out doctors all the time. You could see them a mile away. They were like extras from The Walking Dead; zombies who actually wanted to be put out of their own misery. These doctors never smiled. They didn't make eye contact. They were socially inept. They were increasing in numbers and we were becoming just like them.

I truly believe that the public doesn't understand what physicians do every day. We never had a reason to educate them before. All patients ever see is their doctors come into that small room, listen to their stories, hopefully give them some help, and then leave. Unfortunately, outside of that sterile box is where their physicians are constantly doing more and more work and losing their passion for their job. Doctors have lost freedom, independence and control.

Now you can turn to the industrialized model to fix you, but I would caution you. For one, that is the system that broke you. Second, you will be tagged as being impaired, which stigmatizes you. Though the hospitals see the need for peer support and workplace interventions for impaired physicians, they are well aware that it can lead to more reports to each State Board of Medicine about these physicians. This subsequently leads to more actions taken by those boards (they have a quota to keep). This in turn leads to more doctors having to tell each insurance company about those actions or complaints. The doctor will also have to report those complaints on every application to a new job or new license in another state. Oh, and each State Board of Medicine will have to publish this information publicly on their websites (they have public pressure on them) which will lead to patients reading about it, which will in turn help them in lawsuits against said doctor or help to kill his or her practice. Any question now why suicide rates in physicians are skyrocketing?

The truth is that being a physician is not easy. There are thousands of physicians out there on the front lines giving it their all every day only to be overburdened with minutia unrelated to actually treating a patient. There is so much that goes on outside the patient's room that the doc can be on edge even before he starts talking to the patient. Doctors are human and if you cut them, even metaphorically, they will bleed like everyone else.

But you went another way and reimagined healthcare! You understood that this game, as an employed doctor or one that bills the insurance companies, is unwinnable. How do you win something that is unwinnable? You can't game the system, but you can change the game like Kirk did with the Kobayashi Maru.

The Kobayashi Maru is a training exercise designed to test the character of cadets in the command track at Starfleet Academy. The test's name is used to describe a no-win scenario, or a solution that involves redefining the problem and testing one's character.

As physicians, we are going through our own Kobayashi Maru. Let me explain. We have put ourselves into a no-win scenario. In the original Star Trek example, the cadet has to rescue the civilian vessel Kobayashi Maru in a simulated battle with the Klingons. The disabled ship is located in the Klingon Neutral Zone, and any Starfleet ship entering the zone would cause an interstellar incident. The approaching cadet crew must decide whether to attempt rescue of the Kobayashi Maru crew – endangering their own ship and lives – or leave the Kobayashi Maru to certain destruction. If the cadet chooses to attempt rescue, the simulation is designed to guarantee that the ship is destroyed resulting in the loss of all crewmembers. In our scenario, our patients are in the neutral zone and the hospitals and insurers are the Klingons or Romulans or both. Any attempt at fixing our scenario, in today's healthcare model, ends with our own destruction and the demise of our patients.

In order to beat the "game", soon-to-be Captain Kirk reprogrammed the simulator so that it was possible to rescue the freighter. So, in essence, he never really faced the no-win scenario. But Kirk states he doesn't believe in such a thing as a no- win scenario and the beauty is that despite having cheated, Kirk was awarded a commendation for "original thinking".

The way the healthcare system is set up now, it is unwinnable. Since physician organizations are impotent and the administrators and insurers have control, we cannot beat the game as it is. But, like Kirk, you do not have to give up that easily. The only way to reprogram the system is to walk away from it and practice medicine on your own terms. I did this by opening up my own Direct Primary Care office. It is flourishing. Call it original thinking or call it desperation, it doesn't matter. I am on the other side now and telling you there is a way to win the medical version of the Kobayashi Maru. You can't game the system (by fudging numbers and hiring teams), but you can change the game.

Everyone and their uncle is trying to capitalize on our broken healthcare system. They think they can fix it. Even the techies think they have an answer. They don't. Why? It's simple. They are all trying to reimagine healthcare by keeping the insurance industry and the government in the equation. That problem is unsolvable because they are the problem! Now remove the insurance industry. Remove the government. Let's say everyone has some catastrophic plan that is reasonable in cost. You can't tell me this is impossible to do. Until you pay the first $5000, which is the deductible, of your own money (and maybe that is less depending on income), you are on your own. Let me repeat that. NOTHING IS COVERED! Guess what would happen? Patients would shop around. Doctors would be paid in cash and the prices would come down because there is no more coding, no more billing, no more accounts receivable. Since overhead is less, the cost is less. If one doctor doesn't lower her costs, then patients will go to a different doctor who will. Also, patients would only get prescriptions that are reasonable in cost. The cost for diagnostic studies and MRIs come down. This is capitalism and it works.

Now why do I believe this? Because I have seen it work. With high deductibles plans and health ministry plans, patients are shopping around. They are doing it already, and they are doing a great job at it! I have helped them find lower-costing medications by using services such as Goodrx.com. I have found them a place to get a back MRI for $500. I have found them a cardiologist center that does stress echoes for $225. It is happening already and it puts the patient's skin in the game. And it turns out that Direct Primary Care works perfectly with these plans. The problem with the present system is that right now all the savings are going to the insurance companies so that they can get rich!

Remove the government and the insurance companies from healthcare. They do nothing and are not needed. Let's change Obamacare to CatastophicCare* and we will make healthcare cheaper and better for everyone. That's reimagining healthcare. Sure, there are some details and minor glitches left out here, but they are easy to fix and no plan is perfect. But I would put this concept against any other idea out there that plans to remove doctors, reward insurance executives or let administrators be the gatekeepers of healthcare.

Here is the best part. The doctors are happy in this system. They have some control again. Patients are happy because they get better care. Their doctors are personable, accessible, and comprehensive. They are no longer zombies. They smile and relate to their patients. This is why you want to go into Direct Primary Care. This is why you will not burn out.

2. Which Quality Metrics Really Count?

I was once asked by a hospital administrator which metrics I used to determine my quality of care. I answered, "If they don't like my care, they leave. That is my only metric." She didn't get it but at least she shut up and never said another word. That was a big win for me. The truth is that no one gets what metrics means for medicine anyway. Why? Because quality metrics have been unproven. If a doctor has 100 patients with high cholesterol and after a year 33 have normal cholesterol due to medication, 10 have worsened cholesterol after medication, 20 have better cholesterol due to diet alone and 37 have worsened cholesterol due to diet alone, what kind of doctor is she? The answer is who gives a shit. Should she push higher meds? Should she work harder on dietary counseling? Should patients be more compliant with meds or diet? Yes and no. There are no perfect answers here. Do you understand now?

The whole quality movement is a conspiracy about trust. There are entities out there that hate the fact that doctors are trusted by patients. In fact, 79% trust us. That trust equals control, and these entities are driven crazy by this. It kills them. Who are these entities? They are the hospitals and their administrators, the government and lastly, the insurance companies. How dare patients have allegiance to their doctors, they think. We need to break that trust, they believe. Do they really care more about patients than doctors? No. It is about money, and it behooves them to continually chip away at the patient-doctor relationship. And it is working. More and more patients are identifying hospitals and clinics as their source of healthcare and not a particular doctor.

How else are they trying to fracture our relationship? Well to break that bond, they first need to create patient mistrust. This has a nice aftereffect for them because it validates their existence as administrators. To create patient mistrust you need data. That data is quality metrics. Quality metrics have NEVER been proven to show which doctor is better or worse. They just enable others to take control from doctors and justify why they, as administrators, are being paid so much. The goal is to lessen our power and give administrators something to feel important about. These administrators are now hiring other administrators so it has gotten to the point that there has been a 3000% rise in their population. They are reproducing faster than the tribbles on Star Trek. They are Administribbles!

These fake metrics have given control back to the Axis of Evil (insurance companies, the pharmaceutical industry, and administrators). By creating guidelines that doctors must follow it implies that doctors never knew what they were doing. Hogwash. These supposed poor "outcomes" have so many confounding variables that no one knows what they mean anymore. It's all a ploy but the media buys into it. Remember when the older TV shows always portrayed doctors as good? Now the new TV shows try to make us look bad. Doctors have drug problems, attitude issues or personal strife in their lives. Though the public still trusts us, these shows and these administrators continue to work the public, and like water on a rock, they are wearing us down.

All of this fabricated mistrust creates the illusion that doctors need to be watched like kids. How does all this affect patients? They lose allegiance to doctors and this fractures that all important doctor-patient relationship. In fact, now we are just called providers by them.

This has to stop. In the industrialized model it won't change, but with the DPC model that level of trust that doctors and patients used to have for each other exists. People are paying you so you must prove your worth to them. That does not mean giving them everything they want like the celebrity doctors do (i.e. Michael Jackson's doctor). This means coming through on your promise. By being caring, knowledgeable and accessible, you are building that doctor- patient relationship. You are no longer just a provider. You are an actual doctor again. These are the metrics I care about. This creates a connection between patients and their doctors. That bond cannot be translated or defined. Administrators hate this. They also hate that we have one metric that they CANNOT compete with us on. That is the metric of time. That simple measure may be the most important one to judge doctors, yet it is never used. I tried to see if anyone was using this metric, but "time with patients" was nowhere to be found. Isn't that weird? The more time you spend with the patient, the better job you will do. Why isn't that measured? So let's abbreviate this as TWP for Time With Patients. This goes against the industrialized medicine model. I know because I was there in my former life. I would churn them through. I would borrow time from the healthy 25 year old to give to the Medicare chronic and so on. The truth is you cannot bend reality and pretend rushing through the patients is still giving great care. It wasn't for me. Now that I live in a different model/world, TWP is important. People bring things up that are relevant to their health. I understand the family dynamic. I know their jobs. I know what they eat and if they exercise. I can teach them things and vice versa. I can send them references via email and vice versa. I give them time. And I am a better doctor than I was. That metric, TWP, cannot and will not be ever measured by the insurers or the government because it would shatter the myth of how they define quality. So tell me if you find an advertisement or website where the "system" brags TWP or time the doctors spend with patients? Oh, yeah, do not count concierge or Direct Primary Care practices. We all do that. It's a given.

3. Read Up and Follow Up

Things definitely are different in a DPC practice as compared to the industrialized model. In the industrialized model, you will burn and churn. You also have no time to prepare for patients. It is unheard of to spend time reading your past notes prior to the patient coming in. In the DPC model, however, you do have time, and I recommend you read up and follow up.

Reading Up

Your patients want to know that you:

Remember who they are .

Remember what you talked about last time they were in.

Care about them.

Don't treat them like a number.

Are not wasting their time by having to give you all their symptoms and history over and over again.

I am embarrassed to admit that in the old days, I would just wing it. I may have scanned the chart as they started talking to refresh myself and then confabulate in saying I remembered our last conversation. I rarely did. How could anyone remember someone after seeing 400 patients over the past month since you last saw that patient? Or, even worse, if it was a year later and I had seen 5000 patient visits since I had seen them last. It is impossible and another reason to do DPC.

In the DPC model you see fewer patients between patients. And, with your panel size so much smaller, it is possible to actually remember your patients. Hooray! So, my recommendation is to go through his or her chart for a few minutes before the visit. Bring up personal and pertinent things like, "How was your trip to Europe?" Make this a habit. An EMR that allows a picture on the chart helps too. Familiarize yourself with their problems, their stories and their past interactions with you. The goal is to get them to say, "He really knows me." And this is good medicine, too.

Following Up

The next piece is critical. This part blows the minds of your patients. The old model is based around "treating and streeting". In others, get it done and forget about them. In the DPC model, it has to be different. I recommend you make sure you spend time sending emails (or making calls) at the end of the week, following up on your patients. It doesn't have to be everyone. In fact, that would be overkill. Instead, just target the ones you really might be worried about as well as a few that you know will make a statement. Even simple earaches or sprains are worth an email that says, how is your _____ doing? Patients love it. They tell others. And it is good medicine, too.

So, in summary, if you READ UP and FOLLOW UP every week you are way ahead of other doctors in your community. It makes you and your practice stand out, and it makes your care better. Isn't that important?

4. You Will Make Mistakes

Please understand that you do not know everything. You will make mistakes. You will piss some people off. This is called life. You cannot know everything out of the gate. All you can do is learn from your mistakes. This means having a weekly meeting with your staff to go over things:

What did you do right?

What could you do better?

Are there any broken windows in the office?

What is our marketing plan or effort to get the word out?

So, am I clear here? When you start, you will not have a great model of efficiency of moving patients in and out. You will not have a great way to get back to patients. How will you know if patients went to their specialist's office? How much time do you really need for a 4 year-old well child check?

The answer is you guess, you work on systems, you trial and error and you give it time. Yes, time. You will need that. And it is just another reason you don't want all 600 patients joining right away. You will have a flawed system, and that will turn patients off. That reputation will spread like wild fire.

Are there any great ideas on how to get your physical office, you systems, your triage, and your style up to par more quickly? Well, maybe this book will help, but I can't guarantee that. The most important thing to remember is to be a doctor first. What does that mean? It means no matter how badly the office is screwing up in its infancy, you still need to perform at least the standard of care if not more. So, when the phones are going crazy or you are still figuring out the new EMR, you still need to keep paper notes and post-its on who to follow up on and what to research and what to brush up on. As long as you do your part as the doctor, the office and the team and the rhythm of the office will find itself.

But you will make mistakes. You will feel like a loser. You will feel like a failure. Remember, though, and this is why I am writing this, we have all made these same mistakes. It takes a year if not two to get seasoned and get your sh%t down. Take it slow. Live on Ramen noodles while you cut your teeth and keep trying to get better. And you will.

5. It's Going to Be Okay When Patients Leave Your Practice

One of the hardest parts of this job is trying not to lose patients while trying to grow your practice. It hurts financially. It hurts emotionally. My advice to you is to get used to it. Do not take this personally. You will. I did. Don't. Patients are going to leave your practice.

I understand how hard this is to hear because I have been there. I probably lost 50 patients over the first year and that is a lot of people. Even seeing that number now blows me away. It hurts your self-esteem. It makes you question what you are doing. But you have to move on. The truth is that there are many reasons people leave your practice. They include such things as:

Your practice is just not financially feasible for them.

You can debate that they should drop the large cellphone plan or stop going to Starbucks so often, but it is what it is.

You are not doing enough for them.

Some people are looking for the Fountain of Youth or Holy Grail or just the "one" reason they are feeling poorly. You were just one stop on their journey.

They are changing insurance policies.

This happens usually around the first of the year. It may be a good time to put out an email explaining to them that joining another practice with their office visit fees and copay and expensive labs may be just as costly or even more costly.

Their new policy is an HMO and you are not in the narrow network and so you are not able to do referrals, etc.

This sucks and it is a reality. Insurance companies are evil. The ACA just gave them more power.

The patient is moving.

If this is one of your long-time regular patients then fine. But if it is a few months after they join, then it was a scam.

Of all these, only a few are related to something you can change.

First, you do NOT want to lower your practice fees. In fact, there is evidence that people would value you or clamor for your services more if you were even more expensive.

The second issue should be a learning point for you. Don't take some of these patients on. They will never be happy. If you do take them on as patients, then warn them up front that you guarantee nothing and then do your best.

The insurance issue continues to be a problem. I don't have answers for that right no,w but the bottom line is that patients can choose cheap and crappy care at other offices or get the best care at your office. Recommend they choose the PPO option and continue with you.

Lastly, there is a lot to learn from your customers but, to be honest, it is not easy to hear. For one, it is an ego thing. You truly put your heart into this business and, unlike in past practices, this is your baby. You take it very personally when you ask a patient why he is leaving and he takes a swipe at you. It happened to me twice. One guy was a jerk the moment I met him, but it was early in my practice and I didn't select well. The other was a couple who could not be satisfied but even then I didn't see the response to my email coming. Pure nastiness. I will go into more detail about these and others in my section on "difficult patients."

We try to analyze why someone has left the practice. It is a good business practice. The truth of the matter is that no one blames himself for anything. Read the first chapter of Dale Carnegie's *How to Win Friends and Influence People* and you will understand what I mean. Doctors tend to never blame themselves in general. However, as a DPC doc, you will probably take things to heart more than then ever before. That being said, many patients won't blame themselves either. If you question why they are leaving, they may not want to admit that it was financial or whatever, and they will subconsciously pick out the time you were 5 minutes late or that you never addressed their hangnail (though you did handle 40 other issues). I bring this up because I no longer send an open letter asking why they left. These can hurt and it is not going to make you better, trust me. I leave it with something to the effect of:

"I am so sorry your are leaving the practice. I wish you the best health in the future."

In this way, I didn't ignore them, but I didn't get down to nit picking either. These recommendations are obvious when it is a patient you really didn't mind leaving. It's the ones out of the blue, who you really liked, that will tempt you to ask. Don't do it. They will hurt more. Since many of you will not listen, I would just love your feedback on this to see if I am wrong.

To summarize, you ARE going to lose patients. It sucks a lot more in the beginning than after a year. Trust me. When you lose a family of four and you only have 80 patients, that hurts you. You are wondering whether you made the right choice, you are wondering how you are going to pay the bills and you are wondering whether you suck as a doctor or not. When you have 300-400 patients, losing a few just doesn't sting anymore. The truth is that it's ever rarely about you. Most of the time, it is their issue. Remember, you are the best family doctor in town because you truly know your patients, you care about your patients, and you have the time to get the job done. They are losing more than you are when they leave your practice. Be confident. Be proud. You are doing a great thing.

The other reason that I skirted around about this is that sometimes patients leave because you wanted them too. These are difficult patients and I discuss them in more detail next.

Update: This issue is so important for your morale that I decided to write an entire book on it. Please get *Slowing the Churn in Direct Primary Care While Also Keeping Your Sanity*. It really will help you. Let me also add here that you have to make sure you tell patients they need to give you a 30 day notice. I really pushed this after not doing it for few years. I lost thousands of dollars by not charging people their last month with us. I talk about this in the "churn" book in more detail.

6. Taking Patients Back

You are always looking for patients to fill up your panel. After a few years, it will just be a waiting list. One question that is difficult to deal with is taking back patients who left the practice. Here is what I do.

Do I like the patient?

If not, then just refuse and send a nice email that says, "I am sorry that I will not be able to take you back into my practice. I wish you all the best health in the future." You see what I did there? I never said why. There is no reason to hurt their feelings. Now, if they ask why then it is up to you. My thought it is to not go down a bad road. Make something up. Maybe you are filled. Maybe you feel their situation is beyond your expertise. Whatever. And no matter what, DON'T GIVE IN!

Am I equivocal about the patient?

Well, I say if you need the numbers, then take them back, but you should have some penalty for leaving. Why? Because people who bounce in and out basically break our whole model. In fact, I would only take a patient back once and that's it. As far as the penalty, that is up to you. I charge my registration fee again and call it a reactivation fee. Some just call it another registration fee. Other DPC docs take two or three months of fees and add that up. Do not be surprised, by the way, if the patient gets pissed about it. Isn't this fun?

Do you really like the patient?

The best part about your practice is that you own it. I have no information anywhere stating what I will do about a patient wanting to come back. If I really love the family and the story is really heart tugging then I may not charge them anything to come back. That being said, if they do leave again they are done.

Most patients can be trusted, but some do try to game the system. Here is the nice part. You are the system. It's your game.

Try to be consistent and do what's right for the practice and not what's right for your wallet. There are extenuating circumstances for every patient. Ask you staff. Maybe that patient was rude to your nurse behind your back. You don't want that person back...ever. Make sure your team votes or gives their opinion on any patient coming back into the practice or you may gain a jerk and lose a great staff member.

7. Difficult Patients

In any other business, the golden rule has been that the customer is always right. Nowhere is that more UNTRUE than in medicine. Why? Because giving patients anything they want may not make for good medicine. In fact, it could kill them or lead to addictions, side effects or unnecessary procedures.

The bottom line is that patients are not trained physicians. They didn't do four years of medical school and years of residency. They haven't seen thousands and thousands of cases to compare to. Wikipedia isn't a reliable substitute for this training. This doesn't mean patients' opinions and input are not valid. It just means that our input is just as valid, if not more. A case in point is a patient demanding an antibiotic for an obvious virus. If the customer was always right then in this scenario, which occurs thousands of times a day across this country, that patient would walk out the door with a Zpak or Augmentin and pretty soon our country would have no useful antibiotics left. This example holds true for patients tick bites as well. Little secret, not every tick bite needs Lyme prevention. How about MRIs and CT scans or other expensive diagnostic tests? If they are not warranted, then they should not be ordered. Will that piss some patients off? You betcha. But it is the right thing to do. Trying to make them happy could create extra expense for all of us as well as lead to wild goose chases after finding false positives. That just creates more problems in the long run.

The doctor-patient relationship is a very unique one. With a good relationship built on time and trust, many patients will listen to the advice of their physicians and the issue of who's right and who's wrong does not come up. Disagreements can still happen, but they are rare and they can be resolved. When there is no relationship, however, there can be animosity and distrust both ways. This occurs with new patients or patients going to an ER or urgent care. I have been there, and there is no way to make everyone happy. What happens is that the doctor just gives in to move the unhappy patient out.

Here is the real golden rule. You need to treat each patient to best of your ability regardless if it makes him or her happy or not. Making every patient happy could turn you into a pain pill doctor. Making every patient happy could turn you into a disability doctor. No, patients are not always right. Neither are we, but all we can do it give our best effort and follow the ethical and moral compass that we have as physicians.

So why am I telling you this? Well, the overwhelming majority of your patients will be wonderful. That being said, you will have some difficult patients. Here are a few:

Users

These patients are testing you to see what they can get from you before they leave. They may join for a month, come in as soon as possible, and then leave. Beware and do not let them bully you in to scheduling everything right away.

Abusers

These patients try to make you feel bad at every moment because you are not living up to their standards. They will email you all the time. They will come in all the time. They will never be satisfied.

No meds for me

Some of your patients hate the fact the medicines exist. Big Pharma is evil, which may be true, but they don't take into account the money being made by supplement companies, naturopaths, etc.

Home Bound

"Do you do home visits?" I get asked all the time. Sure. Then they respond that their relative wants them for every visit. Then I explain that I only do them for certain emergencies. Don't be guilted into doing things you don't want to do.

These are only a few. You will find more. Some will just have an attitude when they come in. Some will scowl. Some are just plain jerks. My recommendation is to find a way to get rid of them. Ask them why they are not happy. Offer to give them back some of their money if they want to leave. It is not worth it. This job is tough enough without having these people aging you faster and taking your energy away from all your really wonderful patients.

8. Get Some Friends

Having your own business can be not only stressful but lonely as well. You have no colleagues to bounce ideas off of. You have no one to commiserate with. You have no one to laugh with who understands the medical stuff you are dealing with. You will want to prepare for this and fix it.

First, you do want to get some peers involved with your practice. Maybe this is a partner, but it doesn't have to be. That may be in your future, but getting feedback from someone doing what your doing is really important. I would expect that is why you got this book and I do hope it helps a little.

You may think that regular doctors doing the industrialized medicine route are your peers, but their journeys are different than yours. They are worried about useless metrics, fighting with their administrators, getting the codes right, etc. You are not in their world anymore. In fact, many have Death Row Syndrome.

So what is this Death Row Syndrome? Simple, all the guys on death row are buddies because they have same fate. When one guy gets pardoned, like you did when you left to do DPC, the rest of the death row inmates hate you. Why? Because they are still going to die. You are not.

How about the local hospitals or private practices? Will they be your friends? Probably not. No organizations are going to support you because you are competition for them. This includes local hospitals all way up to the AMA and AAFP. They may talk a big game, but trust me, you are on your own. In fact, don't be surprised if their jealousy doesn't cause them to try to sabotage you.

You need someone who actually can talk real medicine with you. You need someone who can understand and care about patients' complaints (something you should worry about now). Even if you're alone, and maybe especially if you're alone, you really want to try to get some colleagues who are doing the same thing. That means us Direct Primary Care doctors.

Other DPC docs have gone through much of what you are going through. You must know that because you bought this book. That being said, being able to commiserate with a peer and not staff is important. What helped me was to create a private Facebook group of trusted DPC doctors. I recommend you do the same.

So what else is there? I think that by getting out and talking to the community you may find like more like-minded docs who could eventually join you. Also, there is a host of other alternative health providers who do their jobs for cash who also may be helpful.

In the first version of this book I hoped that some organizations would arise out of DPC strong enough to create an associations for just us. I think the DPC Alliance is it. I highly recommend you join it but even if you don't, please don't ignore this section. Friends and colleagues are important. They ground you. They make you feel that you are doing the right thing. They help your confidence. You will need them. So should you grow bigger in order to get some colleagues?

9. Do You Really Want to Grow Big?

I think the answer to growing bigger depends on you. There is a certain loneliness in being a sole proprietor. Sure, you have staff but having colleagues to talk to is important. Having a partner after discovering your independence can be a bummer at times too. After finally getting the freedom you craved you now have to run your decisions by someone else. That can suck.

So what is the answer? Initially, my personal feeling was not to get big. I kept my office a one-doctor operation. I have come to be more open-minded. Getting some time away from the office that is guiltfree would be nice. Speaking to another doctor without the fear of being judged would be nice. The question is how big do you want to get? I do not know. I asked Josh Umbehr at Atlas.MD, and he was kind enough to give me his thoughts. Here they are:

To grow or not to grow...that is the question...whether is nobler in the mind to suffer the slings and arrows of outrageous fortune...

Yeah, Google told me that.

My thought processes here are two-fold:

To build good software for growing practices, I'd have to just do it. The difference between 2 & 3 clinics is marginal, but the difference b/w 1 and 2 is enormous. Just couldn't do the software justice if I didn't experience those nuances first hand.

Continue to prove that DPC is growing – show that it's more than just a flash in the pan, solo doc kind of thing. That (when done correctly) this can really grow and compete with the status quo.

Other benefits are that I got to hire some old friends, which is always fun.

Prove our "dominance" in our market (this town is all about the east side / west side rap wars). Seriously! West siders hate the east side…and we're only on the east side… so opening a west location plays nicely with the local psyche.

The profit per doc is probably $30-$50k , which, honestly, is not "that much" for the effort/risk…and I don't get that until they are full…maybe 6-12 months. Factor in the cost of startup and operations until they are full, and its probably another year after they're full before I'm in the black. Then again, what I spend now, I don't lose in taxes so you could argue that profit comes much quicker.

There is a risk of losing that small doc feel. This is an important issue. I read about 2-3 business books a month (alright, I listen…a 3x speed) but still. So I'm WELL aware that the cycle of growth is pretty much: Start small and be awesome, grow a little b/c you're awesome…expand rapidly…lose that awesome sauce…lose $ and customers…regroup, remember why you used to be awesome, and try to claw your way back to that original feel. So we're definitely trying NOT to do that. My current book is "Scaling Up Excellence" and it talks about this VERY issue. They tackle the difficult trade- offs that organizations must make between "Buddhism" versus "Catholicism" -- whether to encourage individualized approaches tailored to local needs or to replicate the same practices and customs as an organization or program expands.

Which is why we haven't franchised yet. Because we don't have that much money, the movement isn't ready for that, and I'm not convinced it can be done "the right way". Pizzas you can scale and maintain quality etc. but medical care is a relationship and that doesn't scale up the same way.

So, and this is probably more than you asked for, but I think the optimal way to "grow/scale" in medicine is through management. You're a great example – pretty sure if I was a suit that tried to tell you what to do – I'd hear a string of curse words and sarcasm that would make for an HBO special….amirite?!

BUT, the boring stuff, everything but the "art of medicine" you might hire me to manage for you. OSHA. Payroll. Workman's comp. Employee handbook. Reviewing legal forms, staff management, social media, marketing, group purchasing, cheaper malpractice (actually meeting *about that). Lets say that costs you 15% and some stress. And I say, I'll do it for you for 10% w/o stress AND I can promise faster/better outcomes because its what we SPECIALIZE in. That makes you think, right?*

Josh, definitely made me think and I cannot see myself getting very big. For me, it is about the energy needed to get larger and the return on that investment. Sure I may make some extra money, because a new partner would be paying off my expenses part but it would also add extra stressors in you life including:

- Paperwork

- Staff getting along

- Partners wanting a bigger slice of pie later on

- Headaches of just having a larger practice

That isn't worth it to me. I want a small, family feeling with one staff member who everyone knows. This may change, but I doubt it. You don't see Starbucks making their stores bigger. You see Starbucks opening more stores. That being said, having one partner may be the ticket. To be continued.

10. Too Comfortable

A little, rarely discussed thing I see is patients being too comfortable with me at times. Don't get me wrong. I always try to befriend my patients. I ask about their personal lives and note much of it on the chart and then ask specifically how things are going. I have also opened up about my life to patients and my wife even works with me. And she loves to talk! (I am in trouble for writing that). So, having a strong relationship with patients is what you want. Some patients, however, might get too comfortable at times. This will happen to you and you have to start thinking about appropriate boundaries. Now for some examples from myself and other DPC doctors:

I have had patients walk in and act like they own the place. They talk loud, saying inappropriate things and just making the whole interaction, well, uncomfortable.

I have had patients feel they can just walk in any time. "I was just driving by and my throat has been hurting since this morning so I figured you could take a look at it." No, I can't.

I have had histrionic patients who call with every headache, every episode of vomiting, and so on. They want to get in all the time and as soon as possible. This is tricky. The rule is that they have to talk to me on all their issues before I agree to see them for an appointment. My assistant just can't put them in because I cannot let them eat up all the visits.

I have patients ask me to do tasks that they could do themselves. "Why don't you check into these things and get back to me". Not. Most of the time, I deflect their questions back on them, and let them do the research and then we can talk about it together. It is just a hurdle .

I have had patients just bring a friend in and want to talk to my assistant and want to meet me right then and there. There is a give and take in life. If the person truly is a prospective patient, and if I have time, then maybe I will talk to them for a minute or two up front.

I have had patients who were trying to sell me stuff. These are genuine patients (not the con artists who pretend they are going to join mentioned previously) but just happen to have the newest life saving supplement that will save my other patients. I decline politely, and tell them I never mix business with patients. It becomes awkward.

I have had patients stop by my house. No need to say more than that.

You can see where I am coming from here. I recommend boundaries. If it really is a small thing like popping in, just tell them you have a patient and no one patient is a priority over another. Tell them you do not want to delay other patients because of people just showing up. Remind them that for emergencies they have your email, your cell number, and your office number. This is an education thing and they usually get it. I also email people regularly (see newsletter) to explain these types of scenarios.

Once your boundaries are up and they still break them, then you may want to start moving them out. By not giving certain patients a visit EVERY time they want then they may start looking elsewhere. Good. Be nice. Be kind. Be resilient.

Remember, you still want to give great service but it should be for everyone. You will have these patients, but you will find your own way of handling them. Please don't allow yourself to be manipulated. We have been manipulated by administrators for years, and we don't need to have this happen again.

11. The Negatives

Every job has negatives. Nothing in life is perfect. Being a DPC owner takes work and your practice is a representation of you. It is not only business, but it is personal, as well. This means you will take things personally. If you worked as an employed doctor before then many of the things you took for granted are beihrown in your face now. This includes the little things like supplies to the bigger things like getting malpractice insurance and dealing with HR stuff. Trust me, it is all worth it, but not everything is pixie dust and gum drops. At times you will get down. We all do. So, I decided to point out some of the negatives before you see them on your own because you will eventually see them. This is not a complete list, I assure you.

Insurance companies and narrow networking

These bastards try to hurt anyone they can't control. They should love us because we are not charging them but, unfortunately, no. Control it seems is actually just as important to them as profit. As patients choose high deductible plans, which are the cheapest, you would think that plays into our hands. It does unless they pick the HMO option. Those patients will have to get referrals for procedures and specialists only from their approved doctors. Those approved doctors are in a narrow network defined by the insurer, which means they made a deal with the insurer. You are not on their list. There may be an issue when a patient needs a referral. In the future we may want to get a little political and try to squeeze back on the insurers about this. It also may help to get the patients on our side. They can complain about it using social media, or talk to the local papers as well as to the state insurance commissioners. Until then, this is a problem, but it is a problem for any doctor who doesn't join the dark side.

Quality Metrics

Trust me, there will be a faction of DPC docs who will want you to join the quality metric trend. That is up to you. Please don't feel that you need to do it to justify your work. Your training, your experience and your good care are very difficult to evaluate. If you suck, patients will leave. Quality is in the eye of the beholder. Do not think a quality visit, as defined by the insurance company or government, is the same as a quality visit as defined by the doctor and patient. It is not. Spend your time taking care of patients and not trying to please third parties. That is why we went into DPC in the first place.

Vacations

As a DPC doctor you will never get vacation again. Ever. You are stuck to your practice with a ball and chain. I AM KIDDING. There is a small kernel of truth to this exaggeration though.

For years, I had no one else to cover my practice. I still took holidays off and about six weeks of vacation as well. How? Well, for one or two day excursions, I did NOT tell patients. They do not need to know the amount of time I take off. Since I only received a few calls a day to be seen, it hardly effected the whole practice so why tell them?

For days that I took off, I would still have my assistant in the office. She could do Strep swabs, UAs, and even use a small $40 camera from Amazon to get a picture of the tympanic membrane. On longer vacations (I always took two weeks off to go to Maine each summer) patients were warned ahead of time. During those two weeks I did answer emails and texts that were urgent. I batched anything non-urgent. My assistant also gave me a summary via email each day of things that happened in the office. If anything was worrisome, I would send that patient to the urgent care. This hardly EVER happened in six years.

Patients know you are human. They know you need time off. You are showing your commitment to them by telling them and by answering emails, calls, texts, etc. In all my years in DPC, I only had one person leave over this. He was a real jerk who had canceled his labs a month prior to my trip to Disney World. He was scheduled to have labs done during my week off, but my assistant was out sick. We nicely told him we just need to delay it a bit and he freaked out. He wanted us to not only give his monthly dues back but, to do this for everyone in the practice. Suffice it to say he was jettisoned from our practice. Be well.

After 5 years, I helped a young doctor open his DPC practice across town. For my effort, as I charged nothing to help him, I received a friend and another doctor to take acute patients when I was away. This removed the possibility of having telling patients to go to the urgent care in my absence. I still took my emails, calls, and texts. I still had my assistant there who sent me a 3PM email reviewing the day. But this was my choice. We easily could have allowed all messages to go to the other doc and leave me 100% away from the practice. This brings me full circle to the first paragraph.

The kernel of truth above is this: you are always attached to your practice. This is YOUR lifeline and your baby. Never think that DPC is that easy and you can just forget about it. This job is a blessing but also a curse. If you cannot handle this responsibility of always caring for your business, then don't start a DPC practice. No judgment. It just isn't for you.

So there you have it. You can take vacation. I took six weeks. I wouldn't take three months off, but that is up to you. If you overdo it, then you risk losing patients. There is a happy medium, but I am sure you will find it.

Getting Sick

A quick illness like the flu can happen. You may have to cancel the day, but a least you only need to reschedule 6-9 patients and not 25. They will understand. But what about a bigger illness? Yup, that is a risk. Patients ask me about it and I don't have a great answer. I try to exercise and eat right, but sometimes life happens. I have disability insurance but patients don't care about that. You may get paid while convalescing from an MI, but who takes care of your patients? This is another reason to get a partner. Until then, you have to be honest with patients. You could do a lot of work via telemedicine if you are sick but yet healthy enough to work some from home. You could do nothing and suspend billing until you are back up and running. Getting ill, however, is a risk and maybe the biggest one we have in DPC. But wasn't that a risk in your other job too?

Call Burnout

I am on 24/7 and 365 days a year. Things are not that bad, though, because patients rarely call and I know them. In fact, I received only about fifteen after-hour phone calls in my first 16 months of opening my practice and that trend continued for the rest of the six years in my practice. I do get a lot of emails (5 to 15 a day) and it can wear on you. The other issue is the 80/20 rule where 80% of your questions, emails, calls and appointments come from 20% of your patients. It can annoy you. You are human and at times you may resent these people. It is hard because you want to be perfect and timely. So, there is no simple solution here. Getting a partner may help but not much. So what is the solution? For one, do NOT answer every email immediately or patients will think you are Dr. Google and will expect an answer in .04 milliseconds. Also, you may want to really slow the response with certain patients who continually bombard you in order to train them to be appropriate. This also may mean not putting these patients in the schedule every time they want to be seen. In fact, you may want to have a list of patients who are ONLY scheduled when it is run by you first. Self-preservation is critical. From a fellow DPC doc:

I have always taken pride in that even before going DPC, I almost never got calls on nights or weekends because, unlike big box clinics, our office could always take care of people's needs during the day. Therefore, people did not need to call after hours to "beat" the system and get ahold of the doctor and not the staff. While it is still a relatively uncommon occurrence, I am starting to get a few calls on nights and weekends because it is more convenient for patients. I used to lecture patients about the importance of calling during business hours for everything but urgent matters. In some ways, I feel it would be hypocritical to do so now because I proudly advertise 24/7 access as part of the membership.

So, you can see the dilemma. You don't want to be hypocritical but you also don't want to be abused. Well, you now have my recommendations, but maybe you will find some other ones. Send them my way so others may learn.

Regular Burnout

Every job can give you burnout, even DPC. In our line of work it can be caused by what is called compassion fatigue. Sometimes it is from overworrying or trying to do everything perfectly. You want to be the best doc for your patients and that can drain you even though there are fewer patients in the day. Then there are certain patients who join and have a million symptoms, and they want you to play Dr. CSI to discover what's wrong. The bottom line is that it happens to all of us so you are not alone. Here is what other DPC docs shared with me (names withheld):

I have a constant inner struggle going where I feel like I need to fix everything and everyone. I am getting better little by little, but having this model does sometimes make that aspect of myself come out more because I'm making promises to 'cater' to my patients more than in the traditional model. Also, every new patient is a lot of work up front. And being a DO, some patients want a lot more OMT than expected. I work through it by constantly trying to set healthy boundaries, reminding myself that it's not my responsibility to fix or have an answer for everything, and hope that once the building process is done, things will settle down.

It can definitely be a challenge. I often find that with my patients who don't have any insurance, they look to me to be their sole health care provider. Sometimes I have to do some calculus in my head. It used to be that if someone even mentioned having a little pain in their chest, almost all got sent for cardiac testing to cover your butt. Now that I know that doing so could put someone in significant financial distress, I have to think about it more. I usually resolve the issue by asking myself what would I agree to if it were me or my family member. I tell people that, and they appreciate it. I also give them a disclaimer that most other docs would send them for further evaluation, and I am happy to do so if they are willing. With rare exception, they appreciate my honesty and go with the more common sense plan. I have found that this model is making me a better doctor. I refer less and do more in terms of medical management and procedures than I did in the past. Patients appreciate it dearly.

I have good months and then stress months. We are conditioned by years of dealing with insurance companies and bureaucrats. Now we are working for patients 100%, and some of them think we are magicians and we seem to attract the higher needs patients! All I can say is, you're human and be patient and forgiving of yourself and your feelings at times. It is therapeutic to know you're not alone.

I like to joke that patients are the worse part of DPC or any system for that matter because people are human, which means they whine and complain and are needy.

The burnout is real. It is a different type of burnout from a regular insurance- based care but burnout nonetheless. There are a very small fraction of patients who expect us to solve everything and unfortunately I think we are so passionate about what we do that we may come across as if we can.

The whole start up thing is definitely a lot of stress and work. Even though I'm spent and my schedule is much more liquid I do at least feel my work always has a purpose...either growing the business, taking care of patients (the best I can), or trying to blow up healthcare as we know it. But yes, this is not for the faint of heart.

I'm am elated but the reality is that people are soooo flawed. I was annoyed in the system and get annoyed at times doing DPC but then I realized, hey, I'm getting paid to deal with this now! My patient issues are nothing compared to the administrative BS I had to put up with. I don't send people to collections, I respond to repetitive nonurgent communication reasonably but not instantly and I tell people when they're pushing my buttons. Seems to help.

I have invented a new medical term - the DPC cycle. It seems to occur every 6-8 weeks when I just get cranky, disenchanted, and hate everyone and their absurd demands. You're paying me an average of 80 bucks a month people. That shouldn't include faxing a form two minutes after you call.

Contracts

I don't do contracts with patients. This is a risk as some people can try to get all their care in quickly and leave. I will tell you that this rarely happens. Here is one important tip for you. If someone calls and says he wants to join and needs to get in that day, then do NOT do it. This is the biggest sign that he wants to pay that one monthly fee and then stop once you give him his pressure medication or antibiotic. Of all the indicators of membership abuse, the one where they NEED to get in that day is the biggest. Tell them you cannot do it, but there are urgent cares they can see until they are ready to join. You will never hear from them again. If that doesn't work, and they still join, at least you get your monthly fee as well as a registration fee. In fact, that is why we created the latter.

A Grassroot and Cohesive Organizing Body

When I started, DPC was in its infancy. There really was no one governing body to guide us. This has changed with the DPC Alliance, which I helped start. If you don't join, this is another reason I recommend not just using this book as your only reference. Learn from others. Yes, you are out there on your own but even just commiserating with others helps.

Board Certification

This may not be a total negative. I have certified three times, but now I am done with ABFM. I read all the time because I now have time. I do not need to prove anything to them anymore. I definitely don't need to pay for yearly SAMs or do their testing. Get your CME to keep up-to-date and keep your license. Drop the ABFM and get certified by an alternative board like the NBPAS. Just so you know, almost EVERY doc I know in DPC is no longer certifying via the ABFM and their MOC process.

Using Health Savings Accounts (HSAs)

Right now, HSAs do pay for medical services. That is how my monthly statement, via an email and via billing, comes out of my Atlas.MD system and is received by my patients. This, in turn, is what patients will have record on their HSA card account statement. That being said, I presently do not tell patients that they can use their HSA card for my DPC practice. I tell them to ask their own accountants. I also have no way to know which card they put in the system, and I am not there to police that. So, why am I being coy here? The issue of using HSAs for a DPC subscription fees is still unclear.

Some people believe the Affordable Care Act says it is cool to use. Unfortunately, the IRS doesn't agree and could possibly audit patients for this. That is because the IRS is purposely not being clear about this. They have been asked by a bipartisan group of prestigious congressman to clarify this stance in our favor. They have not done so. So what do you do? I do not have an answer for you. Ask your lawyer. Ask your own accountant. Do your own research. Hopefully, this point will be moot by the time you read this, but some DPC doctors are comfortable telling patients they can use their HSA cards for their services. In fact, thirteen states have passed laws to allow this to happen. There is a law pending my home state of Virginia right now. Will that overrule federal law, though? I am not so sure. Other doctors tell their patients not to use the HSA card because of a letter from the IRS in 2014, the most updated formal communication from the IRS, that clearly states that fees for a 'DPC medical home plan' are NOT HSA reimbursable fees AND to top it off, if someone is paying for a 'DPC medical home plan' and simultaneously funding an HSA they may be in violation of present IRS policy. So, as you can see we are stuck in our version of those states that have legalized marijuana. It is federal versus state law. There is a proposed federal bill trying to change this and it is called SB 1989. Julie Gunther MD tells her "patients that, right now, they cannot use their HSA for the membership fee. They can use it for prescriptions, labs, imaging, pathology or durable medical equipment but, with the strictest interpretation it does look like they shouldn't be funding their HSA while a DPC member."

I just recommend you be truthful and as open as possible. Do not make this your biggest selling point. You exceptional care is what gets you patients. Do not put yourself at risk.

Competition

I have a big local family practice group that is very competitive. The administrator there played the typical administrator games. I did work for a year as an independent contractor with this group, and they were nice to me. When I left no one talked to me again. The administrator tried to piss me off by stating in a goodbye email that they will be venturing into DPC soon. It has never happened. What did happen is they blocked my access to the colleges any way they could. Such is life. Remember, the Death Row Syndrome I talked about. This doesn't mean that some docs won't get wise and try to do DPC. Should you help them? I think yes. The more the merrier. They can even help you with call and share seeing patients for free when you are away and vice versa. Also, as I said before, a rising tide floats all boats. It just may help you to get the word out about DPC if others jump in.

Prescriptions After Patients Leave You

Here is a dilemma. What do you do when a patient decides that he no longer wants to be part of your practice? When I write a prescription for meds, I usually give 90 days and 3 refills to save them money. But let's say a patient decides to leave your practice, what do you do about the prescriptions? I have asked my fellow DPC docs and this is what they said:

I have called the pharmacies they used and cancelled them after 30 days. For one, I felt used. Secondly, I am not monitoring them so I don't feel comfortable with them filling their thyroid meds or BP meds for a year.

New patients get 90 days without refills. I have them come back and if they are committed, I give them the refills.

We start them out with 30-days and go month by month until they prove to legit vs. those who'll take advantage of the program. Our loyal patients get 90-days and one refill. Also for those of you that are dispensing out of your pharmacy, only give 30-days, as well, otherwise you have no way of collecting on those meds if you give me. This is just our policy.

I usually don't dispense or prescribe amounts or refills much past when the next visit is due. I have learned it the hard way many times that if I give a year's worth of refills and ask the patient to come back in 6 months, they often don't. Fortunately, that doesn't happen as much in DPC as FFS, but it does happen.

I rarely do prescriptions beyond 90 days unless patients have been with us for over a year. As most people truly need visits or labs for their issues every 90 days, that's usually not an onerous requirement given we don't charge extra for the visit!

I recently had a lady really piss me off with this issue. She'd been a patient for about 1.5 years and had "threatened" to quit several times (due to costs), but never did. She made a visit to have about 6 new problems addressed, that included 2 procedures (knee injection and mole removal) about 1 week later. I also gave her a 90-day Rx with 1 refill at the pharmacy for a med. She called to "cancel" the day after I removed her sutures. I called the pharmacy to rescind the 1 refill on her medicine as she was actually due for f/u lab in 3-4 months. She called me at 90 days when she figured out I cancelled her Rx and called me a "motherf%cking greedy son-of-a-bitch".

I've also had patients request to get their "cheap" meds (prescribed by another doc) with us even after they cancelled. As my dad told me, "you can't fix stupid."

People wonder if there is a liability for not covering them after they leave but the reality is that they left us! You just need to have proper procedures in place. Make sure you have a formal declaration (and notice from us) that the patient is leaving our care/service. Always advice patients to establish care with another primary care provider ASAP and that we will not continue to provide care and prescription past 30 days.

A Recession

What happens if the global economy tanks? What happens if there is another recession? The answer is I don't know. It is possible that people will cut back on everything including healthcare. This includes DPC. I feel that I charge a reasonable fee and hopefully catastrophic plans will someday be cheap again as well. The combination of the two makes the most sense economically even in hard times but who knows.

So, there you go, some negatives for DPC. There aren't that many, but they exist. Is it still worth doing? Hell, yes. Just remember that this job enables you to be the doctor you always wanted to be.

12. Have Fun

I struggled so much with making my practice successful in the first year that a lot of times I forgot one thing; that is to have fun. Though I was happier in my job than at any other point in my life, and my wife can attest to this, I still had issues with letting my guard down. Now there is some background to this. For 18 years, others had employed me. That meant there was no room for error. No room for complaints. I lost having fun with patients because I would worry that they would take it the wrong way. Crack a joke? Too risky. It happened before after which I had a meeting with some dumbass administrator who wanted to show how important she was and how I had to change. I did change and became a drone who rarely had smiled and that made the job a drag. To survive, I actually produced a bimonthly humorous medical magazine called the Placebo Journal for ten years. It was the therapy that I needed. But I digress.

This job is different. I needed to change back to the fun me. I mean, why go to work every day dreading it? I used to be that way. I would lie in bed after a morning shower and talk myself into going. It was a close call every day. But doing a DPC practice is different. This job is a reflection of me and everything I wanted a practice to be. Yes, you want to make patients happy but not at your personal expense. You need to enjoy each day. My recommendation is to find out what makes you smile, what is fun, and what makes you happy on the job. I know you may blow this off so I am going to gently remind you as you to actually sit down and reflect. List out some answers to all three of these questions and answers. Here are mine:

What makes me smile?

- Feeling that I am independent and successful

- Making money

- Seeing little kids

- Seeing people being proud of the changes they are making

- Exchanging stories with patients
- Knowing I became the doctor I dreamed of being

What is fun?

- Actually helping someone
- Appreciative patients

- Laughing with patients

- Making my practice the way I want it to be

- Being friendly with patients

- Hearing great feedback from my patients

What makes me happy?

- Having control over my professional life

- Exercising

- Eating healthy

- Having some alone time without useless meetings

- Having a smooth day in office

- Learning

So, why did I ask you to do this? Because there will be days that you will get caught in a funk. You will question yourself. You will wonder why you did this major transition. Or, you will have some tough life stressors outside of the office. Whatever the reason may be, you need to know that you made the right choice. How do I know that? Give it time, one to two years.

13. Saving for Retirement and the Tax Benefits of Owning Your Own Practice

Let me start this chapter with a disclaimer of sorts. What you are reading is not legal advice. I am not a lawyer nor am I an accountant. Anything I tell you will have to be run by both of these parties in order to make sure it is cool to do. Please nod if you understand. Great.

Owning your own LLC or corporation is awesome. Which one you pick is up to you and your lawyer and accountant. You can write off such things as the gas mileage driving to get supplies or seeing patients. In fact, all supplies and CME trips are also written off. No longer does your employer get to grill you on this. It is up to you and your hired guns to figure this out, but is really works in your benefit. The goal, obviously, is to lower you taxes. So, your cell phone is written off. So is your health insurance. Add to this, marketing for your practice, paying yourself a salary and buying cool equipment you always wanted to try like POCUS and PRP, for example. If you get an HSA, then that too comes off your taxes.

A retirement plan is also crucial. My wife and I were putting our regular $15K or so a year each towards our retirement. But there was one more option that we tapped into. When you get to the point where you are filled, you may want to consider a Safe Harbor 401 K. The following is from the IRS website, but this is always subject to change:

A 401(k) plan is a qualified plan that includes a feature allowing an employee to elect to have the employer contribute a portion of the employee's wages to an individual account under the plan. The underlying plan can be a profit-sharing, stock bonus, pre-ERISA money purchase pension, or a rural cooperative plan. Generally, deferred wages (elective deferrals) are not subject to federal income withholding at the

the time of deferral, and they are not reported as taxable income on the employee's individual income tax return.

401(k) plans are permitted to allow employees to designate some or all of their elective deferrals as "Roth elective deferrals" that are generally subject to taxation under the rules applicable to Roth IRAs. Roth deferrals are included in the employee's taxable income in the year of the deferral.

What does this mean? Well, again, run it by your accountant, but in reality it means you have to have at least one employee (assistant, RN, LPN, MA, phlebotomist) that you are paying who is not a family member, even if you are paying your family member to be a practice manager like I did. Then your accountant will work with you to figure out a salary for you and family member if they are working with you. Once that is done you basically create a profit- sharing plan. You will need help from a benefit manager, another third-party, to do this and keep the IRS happy. You will also need to work with a financial company who is in charge of where the profits are invested, like a 401 K and the Roth IRA. We put money both towards the 401K and a Roth IRA.

This enables you to give your employee a retirement option. He or she will decide the amount she gives to his/her plan each month and you have to match some or all of that. Therefore, you are all putting some money each month away. But here comes the best part. At the end of the year, you can put whatever profits you make towards the retirement in one lump sum as long as you give your employee a small amount of that as well. This amount is discretionary and really up to you. There were times we were putting an extra $30K to $40K a year into our retirement fund. How cool is that? This brought our taxes down tremendously. It also made my assistant extremely happy, and this is one example of how to retain employees.

I will not go into more detail than this. Why? Because it is really complicated and I simplified it here. The bottom line is that you will need your accountant and your employee benefit manager to work the numbers with you regularly. To be fair, you have to pay the latter monthly and it also may raise your accounting fees. It made my butt cheeks clinch seeing their bills, which were higher than my monthly rate for patients, but in the end it does work out in your favor due to the tax savings.

I am not telling you that you have to do this. I am showing you, however, that there is a pathway to save lots of money for retirement. Much more than you can otherwise do, which may make your ultimate exit plan, retirement, much easier and quicker.

14. Selling Your Practice

I know what you are saying, "Why do I want to know about selling my practice when I am just starting one?" You are right, it seems weird. Well, I just want to show you what you are worth. The reason is that I may be one of the ONLY doctors who have successfully sold their DPC practice. Just like I was ahead of the game in starting this type of practice, I am also one of the only ones who now knows how to make a profit by selling it. But I am not that special because I believe this applies to all of you.

The point is that I am giving you hope. You are building something that is worth money. A subscription business is guaranteed money to the person taking over for you. Unlike fee-for-service practices, a DPC office is saleable. Those other practices are hard to even give away nowadays. The FFS doc may be able to sell the structure and equipment but because there is no guaranteed income coming in regularly they are not coveted. FFS practices also have tons of overhead, which includes staff and other things. Even worse, accounts receivable are 90 days out so the person taking that type of practice over has to start grinding right away. They then have to fight with insurance companies to get paid and only then they may start making money way down the line. No one wants to risk that. DPC practices, however, have minimal overhead and the buyer will get a nice paycheck within days of taking over.

For me, I was 55 when I decided to retire. It was just time for me to explore other options in my life. My office cruising for over 6 years with a full panel and I was able to put enough money away to make this decision. This decision was difficult for me and I understand this may not be for everyone. In fact, I only wish I started DPC at age 30 because I would have kept going for twenty plus years. My age and interests have now pushed me in a different direction. I am pointing this out just to show you a light at the end of the tunnel. What you build is worth a good bit of money.

HOW MUCH IS YOUR PRACTICE WORTH?

This is not an easy answer. For me, there really were no precedent in the world of DPC to use as a metric. Other subscription industries, in my research, will sell their business for two to five times gross income. I am here to tell you that this does not apply to DPC practices. Why? Because this industry is still in its infancy. You have to take into account that most doctors are not risk takers. They also have tremendous loans to repay and to charge such an exorbitant amount would be prohibitive to them. I understood that.

The next thing to take into account is whether you own the building or not. I would add the amount of the structure on top of the number you are asking. So what is that number? Like I said, two to five times gross annual income is way too much at this time. Maybe that will change in the future. For me, I had reasons to make this affordable to my buyer. They are:

- The amount needs to be low enough to stop any barriers to entry.

- The amount needs to be easy to understand.

- The amount needs to take into account how many buyers there will be (see below).

- The amount needs to take into account what money I need to get out of the sale.

I decided to ask for an amount that was one time net income. That is much lower than other industries by a long shot. I knew that. Could I have asked more? Yes. No doubt. I just knew that I was comfortable with this number and it was non-negotiable. I made the deal so that I also wanted a $25K deposit on top of this number so that the buyer had skin in the game. My buyer spent a ton of time looking at all my books with his accountant to make sure it worked for him. The accountant, I was told, was very enthusiastic, and we went ahead with the sale. This is another reason I knew I could get more, but I didn't care. Why? The doc taking over was a great doctor who was committed to staying and would be great for my patients. I owed that to them.

Now let's talk about the number of buyers available to you. This one is tough. Selling your practice needs to be a secret because you do NOT want to risk losing patients because they think the place is going to change or go out of business. Your patients believe in you and your care is what they are paying for. They will fear any news of a change. That is how important relationships are in the DPC world. So, how do you find a buyer? I had to put feelers out there in the community in a discreet way. I spoke to another DPC doc in town, who I helped open his practice, to see if he knew anyone. He did. Things slowly progressed from there. To summarize, I was lucky. For you it may take ads in the DPC News, or other avenues, in order to get the word out. Or maybe there is a residency near you. I was limited due to the amount of doctors in town with restrictive covenants by their employers. This crap still exists, and unfortunately, it is a reality. My point in stating all this is that when you find the right interested buyer, you don't want to scare him away with an exorbitant selling price.

THE TRANSITION

The details in the sale are a lot, but they really aren't that hard. I was happy that my buyer went into the minutiae of my books because I wanted him to know everything. I wanted no guilt that I ever ripped someone off and would feel guilty. Once that was done, there was the issue of getting lawyers involved to create a contract. My office was basically sold as a loan that the buyer could not get out of, even if he moved, quit, won the lottery or even died. His deal was set up to pay the total sum on a monthly basis with a very small interest rate over five years. I was not walking away with a ton of money in my pocket, but that was fine with me.

I made the deal so that all the supplies and equipment were his. My staff person was also staying with him and the patients LOVED that. He would be walking in day one with everything set.

The deal was made about three months prior to me handing over the keys. I did not tell patients until 45 days out so as not to scare people away. I sent an email to each one using Atlas, and I also put it in my newsletter and sent printed letters to everyone. We lost two families and that was it. By the time the transfer took place, I had the same number of patients as when my buyer started exploring purchasing the practice.

I won't bore you with the other details as they are pretty obvious. You have to change over billing information for utilities and such. I did NOT own the building, but I did talk to my landlord and convinced him to keep the rent the same for the first year of my buyer's occupancy. Atlas made the EHR transition easy as well with great customer service. Sure there were little snafus in other areas, but nothing too much to overcome. After the transition took place, I stayed in touch with my buyer for a while to hammer out anything else. Overall, it was pretty easy.

IN SUMMARY

I had a great run. I loved my patients and I think they loved me, but in reality, the DPC system is what they loved the most. The personal care by a great doc is what they longed for and they got it in me and now with the doctor who purchased my practice. I feel great about that. Paying it forward in the DPC world means, to me, not gouging or handicapping your buyer with a large price tag while also giving your patients' care to a doctor you are confident in. We did that.

15. Conclusion

This may be the conclusion of this book, but it is really the beginning for you. Hopefully, you now are convinced to take the DPC jump. We other DPC docs want more physicians like you to join us in this revolution. It is time to take back our healthcare system and we can't do it by being employed physicians. Remember, administrators don't want us to open our mouths. They want us to shut up and be their pawns. As a DPC, doc you can truly put your patients' interests first because you know that when you do that you will be rewarded in the end.

Once again, I implore you not to just listen to my advice but to listen to others as well. Read. Network. Communicate. There is no one way to do DPC. This book will hopefully get better as we get better in our understanding of what makes DPC works. Until then you must count only on yourself. The landscape will always be changing because people will hate us. Remember my Death Row Syndrome definition? That means you will have people who magnify any weaknesses they can find in DPC. You have competitors trying to tear you town. You have local and national politics. Stay the course. You will still win because you have been spared from Death Row.

The path back to authentic medicine starts with leaving the industrialized model. This means no insurance, no government, no third parties and no administrators! You did that. You are on your own because that is the way medicine is supposed to be practiced. It may feel lonely, but others have been through this transition and we are here for you.

Let me end by describing a scene I loved in the movie Big with Tom Hanks. Josh Baskin was listening to some idiot administrator rattle off his stats. Now, Josh was a kid in a man's body and could not understand the statistical gobbledygook that the main protagonist was blurting out. It was all nonsensical to him because to kids toys are just meant to be fun. Well, it is the same for being a doctor. All this crap we have to do in medicine is counterintuitive because we are supposed to be helping people, and these nonsense stats don't really address that. After doing DPC for the past year, I dream of myself as Dr. Josh Baskin asking some administrator at a conference:

"I don't get it. Why do you need to see patients every seven minutes?"

What's fun about an EMR?"

There are a million codes in the ICD-10. Why do we need that?"

Can't we have a system where the insurance companies don't make the decisions, and it is just the doctor and the patient?"

The point is that when you are your altruistic self, the same person who went to those medical school interviews, you will ask very simple questions that puts today's dogma in a precarious situation. I am Josh Baskin, a big kid, and medicine is fun again. Won't you join me?

APPENDIX A:

The Healthcare Sharing Ministry

Letter to Health Sharing Ministries

To Whom It May Concern:

The purpose of this email is to simultaneously introduce ourselves, Forest Direct Primary Care, and also to inquire about working together to communicate with your members, as we believe that our services could be a good fit for those in your group who are part of our local community. As a Direct Primary Care provider, we run a system in which our patients get access to all the primary care they need under a single monthly fee. More importantly, we're an operation that enables our patients to have personal interactions with their doctor without being at the mercy of things such as insurance policies, co-pays, limited office visits, or the like.

Frankly, we think we'd be a good fit for many within your system, as we offer an alternative way of getting quality primary care while eschewing many of the constraints associated with normal healthcare. We would like to continue to get connected with those who need our service most, and we think that would include many of those in your organization who are located within Forest or the greater Lynchburg area.

Please be in touch and let us know if you need us to provide you with any more information. We would also be happy to do a mailing to area members if helpful.

Best wishes,

Dr. Doug Farrago

Dear Dr. Doug,

Greetings from Christian Healthcare Ministries! I hope you are doing well. Thank you for your interest in working with our members and the local community to offer affordable care at a reasonable price.

I would like to add you to our recommended provider list (found on our website at chministries.org). This list originally began as a compilation of health care providers who were specifically recommended by members. Recommendations were made based on great service and fair prices. As time has continued, we have begun expanding that list to include providers who reach out to us—with the intent on serving our members fairly.

Based on the information you provided below, I will make sure you get added to our list. If any additional information is needed, such as a website or email address, please let me know and I will add that to the information provided.

As an FYI, members looking for providers in their area are able to search the list by location and preferred distance, so I believe this feature would be very helpful and perhaps field some of the interested individuals for you.

Please let me know if you have any further questions in the meantime.

God bless,

_____ (Name withheld)

Hello Douglas,

Greetings from Christian Healthcare Ministries! I hope you're doing well.

I'd love for you to review the attached letter and send us your feedback. This is what we'd like to email out to members within 100 miles of your practice. Because the cost of sending email on our end is virtually zero, there would be no cost for sending this out.

Please let me know if you have any questions.

Thanks and have a great day!

_____ (Name withheld)

APPENDIX B:
Monthly Expenses for My Office

Expenses

Rent - $1400 to $1700 (over six years)

Accounting - $150 to $200 per month

Atlas MD - $300 a month

Add on for Electronic Rx for regular meds and narcotics - $100 a month

Health Insurance (for family and myself) - $1300 on up. We ended up using a health sharing ministry ourselves at about $450 to $650 a month.

Office Internet and Phone - $125

Disability Insurance - $425

Gas - $50

Water - $15

Office phone - $125

Taxes - $860

Electricity - $50

One Staff Person - $1800

Supplies - $100

Umbrella Insurance Policy - $20

Business Insurance - $25

Tax Prep - $80

Malpractice Insurance - $350

Payroll Taxes - $70

State taxes - $20

Total = approximate around $7400 a month

Year = $90,000. Sounds like a lot, but you are bringing in around $325,000 - $350,000 when filled depending on the average cost per member per month.

APPENDIX C:
Stay with us letter during "Insurance Picking" Time of year

Dear _____,

Well, it's that time of year again. The holidays are upon us, and who doesn't love that? Unfortunately, it is also the time to go over your health insurance options. According to our government, we HAVE to have insurance or incur a penalty (update: this may have changed). Those penalties are getting to be big. You may also choose one of the health ministries and that seems to work for a lot of our patients. For others, you are going to choose the regular options. If you are like me, you will soon learn of the sticker shock coming your way. My family's plan went up 30% this year! This is insane.

Most of you who choose the normal insurance option will choose the high deductible option. Why? The premiums are so high that you kind of have to. Some of you will also be deciding whether to keep your membership at Forest Direct Primary Care. I hope you do and here is why:

For one, you will NOT get better care anywhere else. I am convinced that my 30-60 minutes with you beats a 7-minute visit at another office. And that may not even be with a doctor.

Secondly, these high deductible plans do not kick in until you reach a certain amount, and that can be between $3,000 and $6,000 dollars. Each visit at another office is about $150 plus a copay. Each extra treatment costs, well, extra. A back treatment is $100-$150. A strep or urine test is $25. Freezing of skin lesions is $100 and joint injections are $150, at least. A mole removal could cost you $300. All of these things are included free here with your membership.

Third, our labs are 80-90% cheaper. A recent local office charged one of our patients $660 and these labs here would have been around $60. With a few visits in a year and some labs you would be paying as much or more than our membership fee. Of course, you can neglect your care and not go to the doctor to save money, but I hope you wouldn't do that. That is EXACTLY what the insurance companies want.

What I hope you do is somehow find an affordable health care option and stick with us so you can truly get the great care you need. Your health is worth it!

APPENDIX D:
Letter to Churches

Friends,

I would like to formally introduce myself to your community, as well as offer my support to individuals looking to find a doctor who works for them. At Forest Direct Primary Care, I am offering to provide all your family physician needs under a single monthly fee that forgoes health insurance.

My hope is that you'll find our office visits more comprehensive and personal. Our labs fees are discounted well over 75% and all procedures (skin, joint injections, osteopathic manipulation) are included. With enhanced accessibility, our office will connect to your health in a way that many other offices find difficult to achieve these days. Additionally, we're included as part of the recommended providers by Christian Healthcare Ministries, and would be a good option for similar such systems.

If what we've described sounds like a good fit, then I would love to talk more and get to know each of you that may have an interest.

Best wishes,

Douglas Farrago MD

APPENDIX E:
Email to Former Patients

Dear Patient,

I just wanted to thank you for allowing me to be your doctor over the past year at (BLANK). I hope I was able to meet your needs, and that you felt that I cared because I did. I also want to give you an update on my whereabouts and what I am now doing. After 20 years of dealing with health insurance, I have decided to start what is called a "Direct Primary Care" practice. What this means is that patients pay a monthly fee to be part of the practice. This fee is discounted for couples and families. Included in this fee is:

- Copays

- Unlimited doctors visits

- Full access to me via phone, email and text

- Free skin procedures

- Free OMT (back treatments)

- Heavily discounted labs (about 1/10 the cost now)

I can do all this because I will not be billing or dealing with insurance companies. My office, located in the Forest Professional Park, is called Forest Direct Primary. I am limiting my practice to only 600 total patients. By doing this I can have 30 min and 60 min appointments without the feeling that I am churning through patients.

I enjoyed (_____) Family Practice and this letter is not intended to take you away from them. Don't get me wrong, I would love to still be your physician, and if you are interested please give me a call or email me. Also, if you know anyone who needs a good doctor and would be interested in personalized and enhanced service, then send this on to them, or have them check out my website at www.forestdpc.com.

Thanks again for your time and do hope we see each other again. Remember, the assembly line type of medicine we see now is not authentic medicine but is instead industrialized medicine. Take a look at Forest Direct Primary Care to see "family practice the way it should be."

Sincerely,

Doug Farrago MD

APPENDIX F:
Email Notice (put at the end of each email to patients)

eMAIL NOTICE: The Patient understands and agrees that e-mail is not an appropriate means of communication regarding emergency or other time-sensitive issues or for inquiries regarding sensitive information. In the event of an emergency, or a situation in which the member could reasonably expect to develop into an emergency, the Patient understands and agrees to call 911 or the nearest Emergency room, and follow the directions of emergency personnel.

Email Usage. If the Patient does not receive a response to an email message within 24 hours, s/he agrees to contact the Physician by other means.

CONFIDENTIALITY NOTICE: E-mail is not necessarily a secure medium for sending or receiving PHI and, there is always a possibility that a third party may gain access. Your transmission of information in this medium signals your understanding and agreement that confidentiality cannot be guaranteed. The information contained in this electronic mail message is confidential information that may be covered by the Electronic Communications Privacy Act, 18 U.S.C. §§2510-2521, is intended only for the use of the individual or entity named above, and may be privileged. If you are not the intended recipient, you are hereby notified that any dissemination, disclosure, distribution or copying of this communication is strictly prohibited. If you have received this communication in error, please immediately notify the sender by reply e-mail or at the telephone number provided above, and then delete all copies of this transmission. Thank you.

APPENDIX G:

The following is probably the most important document I ever written for marketing my practice. And I stole it! Well, not totally. Joe Polish is a famous marketer, and on his podcast "I Love Marketing" he allowed anyone to tweak his material for a PDF to give to future customers. I also mention this in a lecture I did at the Nuts and Bolts D4PC conference in 2018. It is the most requested piece of information anyone has ever asked me for over the years.

I give it to you for free here. Just change the names and personal information. Have a designer spice it up into a nice PDF. Then use a pop-up when people go to your site and have them request it. That gives you their email to follow up on. They get a great and proven document showing how bad our present medical system is and how great DPC is. This is a sales funnel. And it works. You can also download my actual PDF that I used at www.dpcbook.com. Shhhh. Don't tell others.

THE CONSUMER GUIDE TO PRIMARY CARE

Read this guide and you'll discover:

- What Every Patient Ought to Know About Their Primary Care Office

- 6 Primary Care Office Rip-offs

- 9 Most Common Complaints Patients Have About Their Primary Care Office

- 7 Costly Misconceptions About Primary Care

- The Top Six Errors to Avoid When Choosing A Primary Care Doctor

- The Top Five Mistakes to Avoid After You Have Picked Your Family Doctor

- Ten Questions You Should Ask When Meeting a Doctor

- The Value of Having a Primary Care Physician

- Why You May Want To Consider a Direct Primary Care Doctor

- Great Care, Guaranteed

- And Last, But Not Least, 7 Steps To Optimizing Your Health

Provided as an educational service by:

Douglas Farrago MD of Forest Direct Primary Care

www.forestdpc.com

434-616-2455

Dear Patient,

Choosing a family doctor isn't easy. Why? Because you're bombarded with misleading advertising, confusing claims, and bad information from the insurance companies, the media, local billboards and others who are NOT physicians but pretend that they are. How do you ever find a qualified, competent primary care doctor? You start by reading this consumer guide. In this fact-filled booklet, you'll discover how to avoid 6 primary care office rip-offs, 6 mistakes to avoid when choosing a family doctor, 7 steps to optimizing your own health and much more.

I wrote this guide to help you better understand primary care. Now, with this information, you can make an informed, intelligent decision. I am a three-time board certified family physician who has been in practice for over twenty years and has seen over 100,000 patients. I know exactly what things really cost and how they are marked up. What I can share with you are some common-sense guidelines, and if you have any questions about direct primary care, you're invited to call us at 434-616-2455. We've dedicated our business to educating patients. We'll be happy to help in every way.

Cordially,

Douglas Farrago

Forest Direct Primary Care

What Every Patient Ought to Know About Their Primary Care Office

Most primary care offices, under the constant barrage of insurance and government mandates, are overwhelmed. Not just the doctors, but the staff as well. Over the years, these offices have added more and more staff just to handle the paperwork and phone calls. This has led to physicians seeing more and more patients just to break even financially. What has come out of this is a turnstile experience or a cattle- herding mentality. Patients are getting less time with their doctors, which has been frustrating for everyone. During the visit, it is not uncommon for a doctor to stare at his or her computer answering questions from third parties all the while ignoring questions from the patient. Patients are unhappy. Doctors are unhappy. The insurance companies, though, are happy because they are raking it in and have what they always wanted – control.

The healthcare system is so broken that these trends are only getting worse. Doctors have lost independence as most of them now work for hospitals or very large groups/systems. They do this to show strength in numbers in order to bargain better with the insurance companies. Independent thought and feeling of self-ownership is gone. Doctors are now part of the machine and are just trying to get through their days. With physicians having an allegiance to their employers, patients have lost the most important advocate for their health - their family doctor.

Unfortunately, no one has come up with good solutions. Why is that? Well, since the 1970s the number of physicians in this country has pretty much stayed about the same. The number of administrators, however, has risen at an astonishing rate of 3000%!

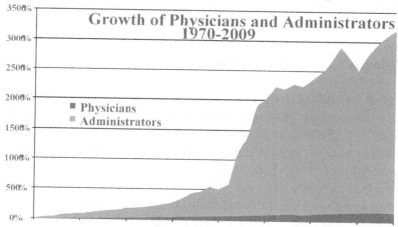

Source: Bureau Labor Statistics; NCHS; and Himmelstein/Woolhandler analysis of CPS

This rate is unsustainable because administrators do not bring in any money into the system. They just crack the whip on the doctors to get more and more out of them. They do this by making doctors see more patients or making them do more computer "chores" to

165

hopefully get some bogus award for their shelves. But where does that leave the patients?

Doctors truly want to help their patients. They went to medical school with an altruistic and idealistic vision. They give a decade of their lives to train to be family doctors. Unfortunately, the environment of today's healthcare system now forces doctors to do whatever it takes to survive. This mean quick visits. This means staring at the computer. This means hiring extenders like NPs and PAs to help with the workload.

It doesn't have to be this way.

Read the following and learn some of the inside secrets to getting the best out of your primary care experience.

Six Primary Care Office Rip Offs

RIP OFF #1: Requiring patients to return to the office to review results when they can be delivered via phone or electronically. Over 90% of the results from testing are normal. The bottom line is the doctor wants another copay and another chance to bill you or your insurance. And with high deductibles that means more money out of your pocket. This does not mean you shouldn't communicate with your doctor about the results. It just means there shouldn't be a cost. With a membership model, like in direct primary care (DPC), these visits don't cost anything.

RIP OFF #2: The office performs a bait-and-switch with the "provider" who is really seeing you. You were thinking you had an appointment with your doctor, but instead you see a nurse practitioner or a physician assistant. You never even get to see your doctor, and it will cost you the same in the end.

RIP OFF #3: Padding the bill. Many offices will perform unproven screening testing that does little except to make them money. This may include yearly EKGs on low-risk patients or a urinalysis at physicals. Sometimes you are nickel-and-dimed for every charge such as phlebotomy, cryotherapy, strep tests, and injections and on and on. These things costs next to nothing for the office but wait until you see your bill.

RIP OFF #4: The doctor will only address one problem per visit or will not discuss any other issues during your yearly physical. Doctors can only bill so much per visit. Once she hits her max, there is no reason to discuss any new issues so it is financially more beneficial for the doctor to have you follow up at another visit. For a complete physical exam, the doctor does not get paid for any extra complaints outside of normal health maintenance issues. Therefore, the patient is told to come back for these issues. Recently, by using a simple modifier in the coding, doctors have started to find ways to bill an extra fee during that visit. Since only a physical is covered for free by your insurance, that extra fee comes directly out of your pocket.

RIP OFF #5: Many doctors are now employed by hospitals. Who cares, right? Well, you should. Hospitals love to hire doctors because this guarantees that they get all the referrals for procedures, labs, surgeries and x-rays. The other benefit is that to the insurance companies and government, the primary care office is now classified under the hospital umbrella, which allows them to charge a "facility fee." This amount can be quite alarming so beware because it will eventually come out of your pocket due to the trend of large deductible plans.

RIP OFF #6: The bill is not paid by the insurance company. This is not the office's fault. The bottom line is that with the new high deductible plans, only a basic physical is covered. Any other visits are on you and the prices are high. Too high. At this point assume nothing is "covered" anymore no matter what the front office staff says.

9 Most Common Complaints Patients Have About Their Primary Care Office

Complaint#1: The staff seems burned out, rude, unfriendly and never smiles. We hear this all the time because, well, they are. The system is broken and they are running around like they are chickens with their heads cut off. The mandates by the government and insurance companies have created so many hurdles and so much paperwork that the staff can never catch up or take a breath. This burns them out and can make them rude or unfriendly. It is no excuse, but now you know why and you also know why it won't change any time soon in this current system.

Complaint #2: You can never get in quickly or you never see your own doctor. Most doctors have way too many patients and not enough time. They hire NPs or PAs to "extend" their reach, but that isn't the same as seeing your own doctor, and they do not have the same training as your doctor. And it still isn't enough. Some doctors have upwards of 3000- 4000 or more patients. That's insane. Most Direct Primary Care doctors, however, have only 600 patients or less. They can see their patients in a proper time period because of this, which also gives them the time they need.

Complaint #3: The visits are seven minutes or less and the doctor is looking at the computer screen the entire time. Due to having too many patients, as noted above, and being asked to click useless boxes on the computer to appease the insurance companies, doctors are spending less time engaging with the patient. Electronic medical records, or what the doctor is typing on when you see him or her, are built for billing and not really to improve your care. The doctor is staring at the computer more to get paid and less to make your office visit a better experience. This only makes the visit more impersonal and less effective.

Complaint #4: I can never speak to my doctor and can only leave a message, which is returned much later, if at all, by a nurse. The combination of being overworked in the office as well as not getting paid for talking or emailing with patients makes doctors less inspired to return your call or email you. Direct Primary Care doctors, on the other hand, have no problem talking with you or emailing you in a very expedient manner. There is no extra fee for them to do this either as this is part of the monthly membership.

Complaint #5: Being badgered for your insurance card, HIPAA form, and copay before you can say hello to the receptionist. This is the robotic system we have built to once again make the government and insurers happy. When your doctor and her staff know you, then there is no reason to ask these stupid identifier questions when a "Hello, Mary, how are you today?" will do. When a doctor is not beholden to the insurance companies and the government, then your encounters are much more personal. This happens every day in Direct Primary Care offices.

Complaint #6: The physician is not conscious of the cost of the tests she is ordering or the medications she is prescribing. Almost everyone has a high deductible plan now, and that means the first $3K to $6K, or even more, is coming out of your pocket. The doctor NEEDS to know what things cost because many patients won't get the medicine or the test if it is too costly. This is bad care. When your doctor has the time, then he can look into these costs and help you make an informed decision and possibly even save you money.

Complaint #7: My doctor doesn't even know who I am or doesn't remember me. With thousands and thousands of patients, your physician can't keep up with everyone. With 600 patients she can. That is the major difference between regular primary care offices and Direct Primary Care offices.

Complaint #8: The waiting room and office is dirty. We call these things "broken windows." If a restaurant had dirty dishes or was messy everywhere, would you ever go back? No. Then why do we tolerate this from a medical office? When the doctor and the staff treat the office like their own, which is the case in Direct Primary Care offices, then you see a real difference in cleanliness and less of these broken windows.

Complaint #9: The phone never stops ringing. Right now there is up to five personnel per doctor who work in a medical office. It's insane. Some just answer the phones all day. Others shuffle paperwork, click buttons or just try to get some things done. The bottom line is that no one ever feels complete because the work in a medical office keeps coming. And the phones keep ringing. And the patients just keep getting more and more annoyed. It doesn't have to be that way. In Direct Primary Care offices, there are no insurance burdens, no billing, 75% less patients and there is a lot more silence. Ahhhh.

7 Costly Misconceptions About Primary Care

Misconception #1: Primary care is simple and any "provider" can do it. Not true, at all. Family doctors go to medical school after a four-year college degree. And remember, medical schools only take the best of the best, and even then they try to weed many students out after the first year. After four brutal years in medical school, the newly graduated doctors will do an additional three years of a family practice residency where they work up to 80 hours a week in clinical situations treating patients and learning. Why do they do this? It is because it takes broad expertise and training to manage things in primary care. Anyone can give a patient a stack of costly referrals and order lots of expensive tests, but a primary care doctor needs to coordinate all aspects of their patients' care in order to get a complete picture of their health care needs.

Misconception #2: Family doctors are just gatekeepers who manage referrals but not real medical conditions. Incorrect! A trained family doctor rarely refers out to specialists. He or she will work with the patient visit after visit to find an answer. Only when she feels she needs help in treating you will your referral be made. This happens only about 10% of the time on average. It takes a smart and confident doctor to admit when she needs help, and a good family doctor will do that.

Misconception #3: All medical care, including primary care, is expensive. This is a myth. The right doctor who uses his well-trained ears, eyes and brain to find a diagnosis is not costly. Most of the time expensive tests and lab work are not needed. Also, when you work with a doctor and office that is cost conscious, like a Direct Primary Care practice, you will be amazed at the savings you will be getting. Most things like procedures, cryotherapy and joint injections are free with your monthly membership fee.

170

Misconception #4: If you don't use a doctor who takes your insurance, it will cost you a fortune. Not true! Why are you letting insurance companies control which doctors you can see? Don't give them that power! Remember when President Obama promised that if you like your doctor you can keep your doctor? Well, let's just say he didn't actually speak the truth. But there is some kernel of truth that people will pick a doctor "in network" just because they think they will save money. The truth is that almost every visit will be $100-$150, plus a copay, with additional costs for any other tests (urine, strep, etc.). With a Direct Primary Care doctor, your costs are fixed at a monthly rate and your labs are up to 90% reduced. You can and should still work through your insurance with your direct primary care doctor, and in the end you just may save yourself a lot of money.

Misconception #5: I don't need a family doctor. I can just Google my symptoms. Wrong. Study after study has shown that the Internet is not the best place to get your answers. Most people find themselves in rabbit holes and get lost with a wrong diagnoses. This just delays you from getting help from a doctor who has been through four years of college, four years of medical school and three LONG years of residency training. If you were able to access your doctor as easily as you can access the Internet, then you would probably go that route. That is called direct primary care.

Misconception #6: Urgent care centers are a convenient and inexpensive alternative when my doctor is too busy to see me or is out of the office. Not true! Urgent care centers may be convenient, but it is not better care. They are also not cheap. They only exist because your doctor has too many patients to care for. At these centers, you will more than likely see a nurse practitioner or a physician assistant. At urgent care centers they will not know your medical history and this often fragments your care. They rarely communicate with your doctor about your issues. It is a Band-Aid approach, at best, and not on the same level as seeing your own family doctor.

Misconception #7: Labs cost the same no matter which office you go to. Incorrect! Some offices run their own labs in house or they own free standing laboratories. Many other offices outsource their labs by drawing blood and then sending the samples to companies like Quest or LabCorp. Those medical offices are charged a fee by Quest or LabCorp, and then they charge you up to 10 times that amount to make a profit off you. If you have a large deductible, then that bill is out of your pocket. We once had someone compare a lab bill from a large university medical center to ours. The price was $1700, not covered by insurance, compared to $115, at our office. That isn't right.

The Top 6 Errors to Avoid When Choosing A Primary Care Doctor

Mistake #1: Not getting an opinion about the doctor from friends or family or not checking out rating sites. To be honest, not all ratings sites are worth any time at all. That being said if you combine their information with what your friends and family are saying, then this information is very useful.

Mistake #2: Not meeting your doctor first. How do you know you are compatible with the person unless you meet him first? Sometimes personalities just do not connect, and that may affect your relationship with the doctor and eventually your care. Most offices do not offer meet-and-greets. Direct primary care offices encourage them.

Mistake #3: Picking a doctor randomly from the list in the insurance company's network directory. Doctors are on their list because they have agreed to a contract that includes pricing, bonuses, etc. Many of these doctors are just fine, but it in no way infers that they are better than other doctors not on the list. Insurance companies have many reasons to put doctors on their list and most revolve around money. Rarely are they vetted to provide the highest quality of care.

Mistake #4: Not picking a doctor at all but instead choosing a non-doctor such as a chiropractor, a naturopathic doctor, a physician assistant or nurse practitioner and thinking they are a qualified substitute for your doctor. You get what you pay for. Training and education do matter. MDs and DOs have the most training. This is not to say these other medical professionals don't have a role to play

172

in healthcare, but they should not take the place of your family doctor.

Mistake #5: Choosing a doctor who refers out for everything. This includes other "providers" as well. A good primary care doctor should be able to handle 90% of everything he sees. If you find that you are being referred every single time for what seems like simple symptoms, then it is time for someone new.

Mistake #6: Choosing a doctor who is burned out, overwhelmed or just doesn't seem to care anymore. If you doctor doesn't smile, remember you or even interact with you, then it may be time to move on. Also, a physician who is not interested in discussing treatment plans with you should make you suspicious. The system is chewing up and spitting out doctors at an alarming pace. Surveys show that most doctors would not have chosen their current career option if they had the chance to do it all over again. The results are just the opposite for Direct Primary Care doctors.

The Top Five Mistakes to Avoid After You Have Picked Your Family Doctor

Error #1: Not seeing your doctor at least once yearly so she knows you. Your doctor is a teacher, coach, health mentor and advocate. Knowing you and your family is part of a greater relationship that will benefit you by keeping you healthy and getting you seen when you need to be seen. Sometimes it takes multiple visits to figure out a problem, and that is the basis of the concept "continuity of care."

Error #2: Assuming your lab or test results are normal if your doctor doesn't call or get back to you. Never, ever assume "no news is good news." One of the most common types of lawsuits is when doctors do not follow up on abnormal tests. When a doctor is responsible for a very large number of patients, it makes oversights more likely to occur. It is a numbers game. Direct primary care doctors carry only about 500-600 patients versus the 3000 or more by other doctors. This makes it much easier for them to not miss things.

Error #3: Being sick but holding back from going to see your doctor because you don't want to pay a copay and office visit fee. This happens way too often and proves the point that health insurance is not health care. You need to use it. The problem is that the copays and office visit fees kill you. With a direct primary care doctor, your fees are covered in your membership, and patients normally come into the office about six times a year.

Error #4: Agreeing to see another provider instead of your doctor. Unless it is an emergency, try to see your doctor (MD or DO). There is a difference in having a well-trained clinician who has four years of medical school and three years of residency training versus those who have just two years of training after college. It is also important to see YOUR doctor who knows you. He or she will not waste time figuring out old stuff that is not related to your complaint.

Error #5: Letting your doctor off the hook for not getting back to you with your questions. Doctors are overwhelmed. They have too many patients and are pushed to do bogus bureaucratic tasks to make insurance companies happy. Those things have nothing to do with your care. Your questions do matter and are critical to your health. If your doctor has no time to answer them, then you should have no time for him or her.

Ten Questions You Should Ask When Meeting a Doctor

1. Will I get to see you when I come in?

2. How long will I have to wait to get an appointment?

3. Are you board certified? In what?

4. How long can I spend with you at each visit?

5. Will you be able to tell me how much things cost? For example, things like prescriptions, procedures, x-rays, strep tests, etc.?

6. How hard is it to talk to you during the day or after hours? Do you text or use email? Are you the one answering these messages?

7. Can I meet you first (without charge) and see if we're a good fit?

8. Will my information remain private or will it be shared with the government, the electronic medical record company or anyone else?

9. Will you be my advocate when dealing with specialists or insurance companies?

10. Will you have to work on the computer during my entire visit?

What is the Value of a Primary Care Physician?

Price is what you pay. Value is what you get. When you select a family doctor you want to know who you are getting, right?

First, you really need to know who is a primary care physician. Don't be fooled by letters. MA, RN, LPN, PA, NP, MD, DO… who is a physician, who is a provider, who is a clinician, an assistant, a lab-tech, your neighbor??? The assorted titles, names and abbreviations don't help anyone make any sense of their healthcare. Add to it the broad use of "clinician", "provider", "practitioner", "generalist" and no one really knows what they're getting. Medical "provider" has taken on a broad range of meanings to include physicians, nurse practitioners, physician assistants and many other trained personnel. The degree of training and scope of practice differs substantially. Here we will discuss physicians (otherwise known as "doctors"). A traditionally trained physician will always have either "MD" or "DO" after their name. Other people referred to as doctors in our culture may be those with PhD's, nurse practitioners, chiropractors, dentists or physician assistants. When most people say they need to go to the doctor, they are usually referring to seeing an MD or DO. And for good reason.

MDs and DOs have much more education and training than any of the other groups.

How are physicians trained? After college and medical school, physicians go on to residency. Residency training is an intensive 3 years where physicians finalize their training and gain expertise in their specialty. This includes family medicine, internal medicine and pediatrics. If a physician stops their training after 1 year of residency they are called a "generalist". When a physician finishes residency, he often takes the last of a long series of difficult exams called "the Boards". If a physician satisfactorily completes medical school, residency and all 4 of their certification exams, including the Boards, they are called 'Board Certified'. Assuring your physician is 'Board Certified' is one way you can assure he has completed all of the necessary training in his branch of medicine. But let's get back to primary care physicians.

Why do you need a primary care physician? While we live in a DIY culture, and I am certainly a very independent and strong proponent of doing-it-yourself, there are a few things that people simply should not do on their own. We've all had an example in our lives of something we tried to do by ourselves and, in the end, if we just would have hired a professional we would have saved time, money, effort and suffered far less trouble! This includes coordination of your medical care. Your body and your health is your single best asset to securing you and your family's future. And being proactive and taking wellness guidelines seriously will help you protect that asset for a very long time. This is why you need a primary care physician.

What can a primary care physician do for you? Primary care physicians can care for most people and most problems most of the time. In any one given day, they may do pap smears, discuss and treat depression, refill medications for blood pressure, remove suspicious moles and diagnose and treat pneumonia, amongst many other things. They epitomize the one-stop shop philosophy that can take care of most medical needs, most of the time. They act as your advocate, your advisor and your coach. They can give you peace of mind by providing the great care you need.

Why You May Want To Consider a Direct Primary Care Doctor?
Direct Primary Care is enhanced and personalized healthcare without the interference of insurance companies. Using a membership model, you get unrestricted access to your doctor and most services for a monthly fee. No insurance is taken or ever billed. This does not mean you don't need insurance. You do for such things as hospitalizations and large procedures. Direct Primary Care doctors will work with your insurance to make these referrals just like any other primary care doctor. The only difference is that Direct Primary Care doctors don't have the burdensome paperwork and hoops to jump through anymore.

(Acknowledgment to Julie Gunther MD from SparkMD for this section).

Why join a Direct Primary Care Practice?

1. Do you want more time with your doctor?

2. Do you want more proactive than reactive healthcare?

3. Do you miss old-fashioned healthcare when your doctor was more of a partner?

4. Do you want more access to your doctor when you need it?

5. Do you want to have a clear picture of your healthcare costs?

6. Do you want cheaper labs?

7. Do you want a nice office atmosphere where the staff is smiling and the doctor pays attention?

Great Care, Guaranteed.

Most primary care doctors have too many patients as it is. They get paid per visit, though that may be changing to a "value" score soon. What that means is questionable. Paying a doctor based upon unproven metrics like blood pressure, weight and cholesterol levels just means he may be more likely to prescribe a medication. That seems crazy. The one thing that will never be measured is what is called TWP or "time with patient." Most doctors would dread this because they are too overwhelmed by paperwork and nonclinical issues. Add to this, the thousands of patients on their panels, and doctors are spending less and less time in the room. That is not good care. What makes it even worse is that when a patient transfers out of a practice, there are ten more patients waiting to get in. So, if a patient leaves the practice, it doesn't really matter that much to the doctor.

Direct Primary Care doctors know that you are spending your own money to have a membership in their practice. They understand how important it is for you to get you in, to be seen for extended periods of time and to receive the attention and care you deserve. No one can guarantee medical outcomes, but Direct Primary Care doctors can guarantee great care. This includes knowing their patients, seeing them regularly, calling or emailing them back and spending time with them. If you leave a Direct Primary Care doctor to transfer to someone else, he does take it personally because he understands how much effort went into that patient-doctor relationship and he wants to learn how to make it better. Patient retention is critical for a successful DPC or Direct Primary Care practice and each DPC doctor strives to give great care in order to keep his patients. That being said, if patients feel they are not getting what they signed up for, then there is no penalty or fee for leaving. In other words, there is no locked-in yearly contract. Why do DPC doctors do this? Because they believe that TWP or "time with patients" is what makes them different and makes their care great. Guaranteed.

And Last, But Not Least,

Here Are 7 Steps to Optimizing Your Health

1. See your doctor regularly – not only for your yearly physical but also to check your labs regularly and to discuss lifestyle changes.

2. Eat Healthy – consider lower carb diets like the Paleo Diet with tons of vegetables.

3. Exercise – both cardio and strength training, four to five days as week.

4. Sleep Better – bad sleep equals bad health.

5. Drink enough water – we are like batteries and if your car battery had no water it would not work and neither will you.

6. Get some sun – yes, sun. Not a burn. Just 10-15 min a day without sunscreen.

7. Laugh, smile and socialize with friends (in person).

Dr. Farrago spends much of his time at Forest Direct Primary Care

 going over all these issues with you because he has that time and understands that your care needs to be personalized.

By following these recommendations, you will gain much of the information you need to make an informed, intelligent decision. If you want a quick and uninspired medical visit where you get very few answers, then there are many offices and urgent care centers that can treat you.

But if you want a trusted doctor who will spend time with you, who will stay in touch with you and who you can trust, then we invite you to call us.

Thanks again for reading our Consumer Guide to Primary Care. I hope you found this information helpful. We've dedicated our medical practice to patient education and service. We will be pleased to help you in every way. We look forward to your call.

Thanks!

Douglas Farrago MD

If you have any questions or comments, or if you would like to schedule a free "meet-and-greet" with the doctor, then please call us at (   ) or visit our website at www.forestdpc.com

APPENDIX H:

The following is for fun and something I collected when asking this question to other DPC doctors.

You know you're a DPC Doc when:

1. You love practicing medicine again.
2. Your new form of currency is monthly memberships. "Lets see, that new set of speakers for the clinic is only 3 memberships, great deal!"
3. You actually get sleep at night.
4. You set your own schedule.
5. You laugh when you get letters from insurance companies.
6. You enjoy the relationships you have with your patients and don't get stressed out when they ask "one more question."
7. Your only true colleagues are a 1200 member Facebook group because no one else in town does what you do.
8. You send a bulk email to let your patients know you'll be out of the office for a week with instructions for coverage while you're gone and you get a ton of responses back to enjoy and have fun.
9. You went home after lunch, with all notes done and an empty in box because no body wanted to come in this afternoon.
10. You are part of these FB pages with docs you have never met, but think of them as your family and friends.
11. Your patients walk out saying "this is the best doctors visit experience I've ever had!"
12. You actually answer the phone at your office. And have to tell the patient 3 times, yes, it's me.
13. End an email with "be well."
14. You have enough time to post on FB.
15. You have watched YouTube videos on how to give a flu shot.
16. You've done patient visits at scenic rest stops, in parking lots, at their office and, or course, at their homes.
17. You finally learned how to run your own strep test.

18. You get super excited for $3 CBCs and $25 CXRs.....and super disgusted by how insurance rips everyone off!

19. You know what Stockholm syndrome is... as opposed to just being a blind victim of it.

20. You don't care what the medical/insurance establishment thinks about your practice model.

21. You can write a full progress note with one vital sign and 3 lines of text.

22. You are excited for the next DPC conference ~ not for the CME, but for the simple fact that you will get to hang with everybody you "know."

23. you have to pinch yourself regularly and say I am so dang happy!!

24. You see patients in your waiting room, because lets face it, nobody's waiting and it needs to get used.

25. You can run the whole practice completely solo. You manage a patient's symptoms and fax in their medication while sitting on your horse and are happy to do so! Or while waiting in the lift line Or at your kids' basketball game. Or in the Target parking lot.

26. You constantly tell the residents you teach at the academic medical center, "It doesn't have to be this way." And they say, "Please keep telling us that." The full-time faculty who have never been in private practice look at you incredulously.

27. Your first paycheck ended in several zeroes, but also started with a zero.

28. The biggest thing you have to do today is choose which superhero band-aids to order.

29. You have time to eat lunch. Even leisurely! Sometimes with friends!

30. You work for your patients not the CEO!

31. Forget drug reps--the patients bring you lunch! Or invites you to lunch! Or brings you 2 dozen fresh eggs from their chickens. I got 2 gallons of blueberries once.

32. YOU ARE NOT SUICIDAL.

33. You have a rockin social life.

34. You get to pick up your kids from school.

35. You go home to take naps at lunch at least twice a week.

36. You open up to patients about the challenges and stressors of starting up, so they promptly pay for a year in advance to help defray startup costs.

37. Mom schedules an appointment for 2 of her kids, brings all 3 and you see all 4 because honestly mom needed it most. BOOM!. And doing so doesn't wreck your day.

38. You do a home visit on a Friday night to place an ulnar gutter splint on a kid who fractured his hand today saving the family an ER visit. Cost to family $60 for the X-ray verses 4 figures in the ER.

39. You have many pictures of patients concerns on your phone that rival those seen in Robbins Pathology.

40. A meal doesn't exist that would convince you to have lunch with a pharmaceutical rep.

41. You see your patients checking their watch cause the appointment is too long.

APPENDIX I :
Small Business Letter

Dear Dr. Hatch,

I thought I would drop you a personal note to explain what we do, and how it may help your business. Direct Primary Care is gaining traction around the country because it allows patients to have more accessible and comprehensive visits with their doctors for a low monthly fee. At Forest Direct Primary Care, we do not bill insurance companies or third parties. There are no copays, office visit fees or procedure fees. Our labs are 90% cheaper than other offices.

As a business owner myself, I understand the issue of covering health insurance for your employees. The cost has gotten out of hand. There are two ways that Forest Direct Primary Care may help you with that. The first is that you can offer to pay our monthly fee ($80) for your employee. This is discounted to $65 per month if you have 10 or more employees joining. This is a nice perk because they truly are getting concierge care at an affordable price. They would still need insurance on their own, however.

The second option is to combine a Forest Direct Primary Care membership with a cheaper, high deductible insurance plan or health ministry plan, and then pay for their monthly fee. This usually saves businesses more than 25% off their healthcare costs while the employees enjoy a much better experience at a doctor's office.

We are in our fifth year here in Forest, and our practice has been filled for the last three years. We are opening some spots up, but would like to see if any local businesses want their employees to take those spots first. Both Fast Signs and Blue Ridge Montessori School are using us.

If you would like to see our office in the Forest Professional Park off 221 to discuss these options some more, then just give me a call or send me an email. We could also come to you if you would like.

Thanks for your time and hope to talk to you soon.

Sincerely,

Douglas Farrago MD

Acknowledgements

We want to thank a lot of people for helping us get this done. Doug's secret group of thirty DPC docs on Facebook was critical for feedback and inspiration. We will not name them here. Jake, my son, helped in the publicationss of this thing and we really appreciate that. Christine Creasey, my assistant at Forest DPC, helped us by helping keeping the office going smoothly so we had time to write. Doug wants to thank all the administrators he has met in life, which inspired him to find a better way to treat patients by NOT listening to them. Doug also wants to thank the old time doctors who did medicine the right way and truly cared about their patients. This is how healthcare should be and can be again....with Direct Primary Care! Check out www.DPCnews.com for constantly updated information on this subject.

About the Authors

Douglas Farrago MD received his Bachelor of Science from the University of Virginia in 1987, his Masters of Education degree in the area of Exercise Science from the University of Houston in 1990, and his Medical Degree from the University of Texas at Houston in 1994. His residency training occurred way up north at the Eastern Maine Medical Center in Bangor, Maine. In his final year, he was elected Chief Resident by his peers. Dr. Farrago has practiced family medicine for twenty years, first in Auburn, Maine and now in Forest, Virginia. He founded Forest Direct Primary Care in 2014, which quickly filled in 18 months. Dr. Farrago invented the Knee Saver, a padding that relieves knee stress in baseball catchers, while he was in medical school. The original Knee Saver is currently in the Baseball Hall of Fame. He is also the inventor of the Cryohelmet worn by people for migraines, heat recovery and head injuries. Dr. Farrago created the Placebo Journal in 2001 and ran it until 2011. His first book, the Placebo Chronicles, was published by Broadway Books. Dr. Farrago still blogs every day on his website *Authenticmedicine.com* and *DPCNews.com* and lectures worldwide about the present crisis in our healthcare system and the affect it has on the doctor- patient relationship. He is a leading expert in Direct Primary Care model and lectures medical students, residents and doctors on its benefits as well as how to start their own DPC practice. He has written two other books on Direct Primary Care: *The Direct Primary Care Doctor's Daily Motivational Journal* and *Slowing the Churn in Direct Primary Care While Also Keeping Your Sanity*. In October of 2020, Dr. Farrago sold Forest DPC and is now retired from clinical medicine. He is still talks to and consults with potential DPC docs on a regular basis. For free.

Debra Farrago M. Ed, Doug's wife, was the practice manager at Forest Direct Primary Care. She was the backbone behind the operation who is credited with keeping Dr. Farrago organized and on task while also helping to create their successful practice. Debra received her Bachelor of Science in Education in 1986 and her Masters of Education in 1992. She is the mother of three great kids whom she was fortunate to be able to stay at home with and raise. Starting Forest Direct Primary Care with her husband was her first foray into the medical field, but one she gladly jumped at in order for her and her husband's dream to come true.